DESERT RAIN HOUSE: Resilient Building, Sustainable Living in the High Desert

**An Ecotone Publishing Book/2015**
**Copyright © 2015 by Juliet Grable**

**Ecotone Publishing — an Imprint of the International Living Future Institute**

For more information write:

Ecotone Publishing
721 NW Ninth Avenue, Suite 195
Portland, OR 97209

**Author:** Juliet Grable
**Book Design:** softfirm
**Edited by:** Fred McLennan

**Library of Congress Control Number:** 2014950763
Library of Congress Cataloging-in Publication Data

**ISBN 978-0-9827749-4-6**

1. ARCHITECTURE     2. ENVIRONMENT     3. PHILOSOPHY

First Edition

Printed in Canada on FSC-certified paper, processed chlorine-free, using vegetable-based inks.

# DESERT RAIN HOUSE

Resilient Building, Sustainable Living
in the High Desert

LIVING
BUILDING
CHALLENGE

# TABLE OF CONTENTS

# FOREWORD

The story of our home, Desert Rain, and its aim to achieve the Living Building Challenge—the built environment's most rigorous performance standard—is at its core a story of personal discovery and the pursuit of a new paradigm for the building industry.

In this book, the author Juliet Grable describes some of the life experiences that have brought us to better understand the earth as a living system. As the owners, Tom Elliott and Barbara Scott, we thought it would be valuable to address some of the underlying thinking that has informed and motivated our journey.

We believe that everything is connected. Nothing happens from a single cause; no action generates a single effect, or has a unique meaning. This is the web of life, but we feel it also pertains more and more to human institutions.

As humans, we inter-exist within enormously complex, dynamic systems. Consequently, we cannot view our actions or decisions in isolation.

Our sustainability choices influence the ecological and physical realm, but these decisions also ripple through our ethical, economic, political, social and technological systems.

In many respects, humanity is facing a bleak and frightening future. From the comfort of our home in Bend, Oregon, we wake each day to news of a world teetering on the edge of systemic collapse; facing political instability, massive extinctions of species, increasing food shortages, dramatic increases in weather-related disasters, and global climate change.

Closer to home, the western lily and the Columbian white-tailed deer are endangered, and less than 500 yards from our doorstep, the Oregon spotted frog is threatened as a species.

But, as a friend of ours used to say, "Things are far too bad for us to be pessimistic."

It is ironic that we live in a world globally connected to an extent never before imagined, and yet we are ecologically and interpersonally impoverished. We know the systems are broken, but how can we change them? As individuals, our actions seem so small in the face of such enormous global challenges. How can we hope to build a sustainable world?

First and foremost, we cannot continue thinking we are building a better world by making a "less bad" version of the one we have created. We have to create a new world.

One of our mentors, Dee Hock, founder of Visa International and a student of chaos theory, had a saying that went something like this: "Complex, sophisticated rules give rise to simple, stupid behavior; whereas, simple, stupid rules give rise to complex, sophisticated behavior."

The Living Building Challenge lays out an extremely simple (though hardly stupid) set of rules or Imperatives to be met. In addition, the Challenge asks, "What if every act of design and construction made the world a better place? What if every intervention resulted in greater biodiversity, increased soil health, and additional outlets for beauty and personal expression? What if every action created a deeper understanding of climate, culture and place; a realignment of our food and transportation systems; and a more profound sense of what it means to be a citizen of a planet where resources and opportunities are provided fairly and equitably?"

From our personal perspective, we do not have a problem "out there." There is no "us" against "them." No evil Empire. We are all continuously manifesting reality through our conscious awareness—through the force of our collective intention. When we look at ourselves in this way, our lives and our actions become incredibly important. Our individual choices are the driving force behind emerging alternatives.

We are reminded of Kenyan Nobel Laureate, Wangari Maathai, who founded the Green Belt Movement. In 1977 she planted seven trees with two other women. She did not set out to change the world, just to plant seven trees, and yet, by 2004 she had planted thirty million trees in 600 communities.

Change of the sort we are envisioning does not happen by "scaling up"—systemic change does not happen by getting "less bad." Ideas like these happen horizontally, scale across networks, and then emerge full-blown as paradigm shifts. We can start anywhere—with friends, with family—and learn what works by doing the work.

For example, some 30 years ago, I converted my family's extensive farm and ranch operation in Montana into one of the largest certified organic operations in the country. This was a deeply challenging and expensive process for everyone involved: cowboys had to adopt new attitudes toward animal health, feeding, and stress-free cattle management; farm employees had to understand and manage soil health and complex bio-systems in entirely new ways; management had to create new markets from thin air, and the family had to step into uncharted territory.

This process was motivated by values and consciousness, rather than profit. Informed by the practice of agriculture, the intention was to live in what the Buddhists call "right relationship" with the people, animals and plants within our

3

circle of influence. Of course, the hope was that reduced input costs, added soil health, and higher profits would quickly follow.

As you might imagine, this move was met by skepticism and derision from peers within the traditional industry. The process ultimately involved years of lonely perseverance and, at times, nearly insurmountable challenges.

However, as a result of the collective and largely uncoordinated efforts of hundreds of similar food system "pioneers," practically every grocery store and supermarket in the country now has certified organic products on the shelf. Eateries from the local hamburger joint to upscale restaurants prominently feature organic and local ingredients on their menus. In short, the entire food system is experiencing revolutionary change.

By taking on the Living Building Challenge, we did not set out to change the world. We set out to build a home for ourselves, what Barb called our "extreme, green dream home." At the time I was merely interested, but Barb was passionate and brought her own special brand of courage, heart and pragmatic voice to the project.

Over time, I fell sway to her powerful vision and with persistence, creativity and substantial investment we have built something much more significant than that original dream home. Desert Rain has become an outer expression of our inner values and beliefs—an effort to live in greater alignment with our core values in a life and world that is fraught with inconsistencies.

Sustainability is better used as a verb than a noun. Like sex and the dishes, it never stays done. The best we can hope for is to create the conditions for sustainability; to foster resilience, the ability to adapt to change; to respond to uncertainty and unintended consequences.

For both of us, these conditions include the practice of being present to the moment, careful observation, robust communication and, most of all, cultivating a sense of humility. We endeavor to make space for what we don't know—to learn to act from our own place of ignorance.

Masanobou Fukuoka, a Japanese philosopher and agricultural scientist once said, "Agriculture is not about the growing of crops, it is about the cultivation and perfection of human beings."

In many respects this thinking also applies to the Living Building Challenge. Our personal beliefs and actions have been profoundly influenced by the process of building to meet the Imperatives of this program.

For instance, we have been increasingly informed by the notion of biophilia—the instinctive bond between human beings

4

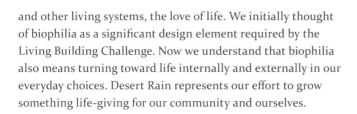

and other living systems, the love of life. We initially thought of biophilia as a significant design element required by the Living Building Challenge. Now we understand that biophilia also means turning toward life internally and externally in our everyday choices. Desert Rain represents our effort to grow something life-giving for our community and ourselves.

Desert Rain is an example of local causality. By taking action in sync with the simultaneous actions of others at a local level, we contribute to action on a global scale. We create change through the force of our collective intention.

Our collective future will not be saved by heroic feats of technology, or building design, or acts of government intervention alone. Both of us believe we will be most successful when we understand our mutual dependencies and value them as life-giving relationships—when those dependencies inform a sense of reality, of human identity and purpose that inspires our collective efforts and our most authentic selves.

**TOM ELLIOTT AND BARBARA SCOTT**

5

# ACKNOWLEDGEMENTS

I first met Tom Elliott and Barbara Scott when they invited me to attend an Open House event at Desert Rain House. As they did then with their thoughtfulness, Tom and Barb continue to impress me with their honesty, generosity and inspiring idealism. I am truly honored that they have entrusted me to tell the Desert Rain story, and to be a small part of the Desert Rain family.

I would like to acknowledge everyone who contributed time, knowledge and spirit to Desert Rain, especially team members ML Vidas, Kristian Willman and Jim Fagan of Timberline Construction, Al Tozer of Tozer Design, Chris Hart-Henderson and Ani Cahill of Heart Springs Design, Rick Martinson of WinterCreek Restoration and Morgan Brown of Whole Water Systems.

Like Desert Rain itself, this book is a collaboration, filled with the voices of many people who contributed to the project. I would especially like to acknowledge other writers who have helped educate so many others about Desert Rain and the Living Building Challenge: Tina Davis, Kelly Riley, and Sweet Pea Cole, Desert Rain's bloggers, and former *The Bulletin* (Bend) reporter Rachael Rees, who wrote most of the articles chronicling the project's triumphs and challenges. Thank you also to Soraya Renner for gathering information so efficiently, and to Ross Chandler, Dorothy Freudenberg and *The Bulletin*'s Dean Guernsey for the images that bring this book to vibrant life.

When I first learned about the Living Building Challenge, I am not embarrassed to admit hopeful tears welled up. Thank you, Jason F. McLennan—and everyone else at the International Living Future Institute—for providing an uncompromising vision of where we need to go.

I would like to thank Michael D. Berrisford of Ecotone Publishing, whose firm but gentle hand guided this project to successful completion, and Erin Gehle and Johanna Björk of softfirm, whose artistic design and layout so perfectly reflects the spirit of the Desert Rain Living Building.

Finally, I would like to acknowledge my partner, Brint Borgilt. I have sought his intelligence, artistic eye, and experience as a builder and residential designer countless times. Most of all, I want to thank him for his unflagging confidence in me, and for insisting that I get enough sleep.

JULIET GRABLE
2015

# AUTHOR PROFILE
## JULIET GRABLE

Juliet Grable's passion for regenerative design and construction began with a visit to a permaculture institute fifteen years ago. A background in natural history and ecology combined with her hands-on experience building a small, sustainable home inform her perspective. Juliet currently serves as the Managing Editor for *Green Builder Magazine*; in addition, she contributes to a number of regional and national publications on issues ranging from watershed restoration to managing urban deer populations. She also writes essays, short stories and poetry, mostly for her own edification. Juliet is grateful to live in Oregon's Southern Cascades with her partner Brint and cat Henri.

# PART I

*Place and Time*

Context for a Living Building
in the High Desert

DESERT RAIN HOUSE

*Desert Rain is a birthing place*
*for creativity*
*for caring for Creation*
*for friendship.*

*...a community of dreamers, planners,*
*designers, builders,*
*craftspeople, artists,*
*workers, helpers,*
*neighbors in Bend,*
*and family from far away.*

**LORRAINE STUART**, from poem
written for Desert Rain groundbreaking
ceremony, July 29, 2011

# DESERT RAIN HOUSE, DEFINED

In the fall of 2009, Barbara Scott and Tom Elliott decided to take a break from their construction project in Bend, Oregon and go back-packing in Arizona. Still in the design phase, the home—which they were calling their "Extreme Green Dream"—was to be LEED-certified, and packed with sustainable features. As they drove across the Desert Southwest, the couple picked up coverage of the Bioneers Conference on National Public Radio. Plenary speaker Jason F. McLennan was talking about something he called Living Buildings. He began by asking his listeners to compare two unlikely things: buildings and flowers.

"Both are literally and figuratively rooted in place," he said. "Unfortunately, that's where the metaphor ends. But I don't think it should." He went on to explain: a flower gets all its energy from current solar income. It gets all the water it needs from the precipitation right around it. It does not pollute; in fact, it creates habitat. And it is beautiful.

"Now, shouldn't this same set of metrics be the means by which we judge architecture?"

Scott and Elliott drove on, transfixed as McLennan laid out his idealistic vision, which he called the Living Building Challenge. The program included several uncompromising "Imperatives." At minimum, projects must produce as much energy as they consume. They must harvest and process all water on-site. They must be made with local materials, and cannot include anything on something called the Red List, a collection of fourteen worst-in-class chemicals and substances.

11

"Without hesitance, we knew we wanted to do this," says Scott. Even then she and Elliott realized that following the Living Building Challenge represented a commitment—though they had no idea of its magnitude—one their design/build team literally had not signed up for. "We were ready to let our entire team go if we had to," she admits. Fortunately, all the players, which at that time included Jim Fagan and Kristian Willman of Timberline Construction, designer Al Tozer, sustainability consultant Mary Louise (ML) Vidas and landscape designer Chris Hart-Henderson, jumped eagerly on board.

Five years and one wild ride later, a new cluster of Living Buildings has bloomed in Bend. Taking its most literal definition, Desert Rain is a residential compound, located on a 0.7-acre parcel on the edge of a historic downtown neighborhood. The focal point is the building called Desert Rain: a 2236-square foot, one-story residence with a stucco exterior, graceful rooflines and a striking curved wall which greets visitors on approach. The wall threads through the building and exits out the opposite side, near a walkway which connects this main residence to the other buildings: a 489 square foot accessory dwelling unit called Desert Sol, a 512 square foot detached garage, which supports more solar panels and houses the rainwater collection cistern, and Desert Lookout, an 815 square foot second dwelling above a garage and the central composting system. The structures cluster in the southeast part of the site; to the north, a constructed wetland filters greywater from all three dwellings. Native plants, rocks and pavers fill out the common areas.

One is struck with how well the buildings fit their surroundings. The warm tones of the stucco exterior; the gentle pitches of the roofs; their scale—substantial, but not monumental—look and feel appropriate for the site, the neighborhood and the greater landscape. The buildings look like they sprang from the rock, and they certainly share the High Desert palette.

Like all buildings, Desert Rain is a reflection of a particular culture in a particular time and place. However, because Desert Rain is a collection of Living Buildings, it is an artifact radically different from the culture at large; hopefully, it is a prescient vision of where society and architecture are heading. The materials themselves tell a kind of regional story. The plaster was made from Oregon clays. The lumber came from Oregon forests and salvaged structures. The steel for the roof came from Washington State and was fabricated into roofing, gutters and downspouts on-site. The rocks for the landscaping were pulled from the site itself, or from nearby Klamath Lake. Even the solar panels were made in Oregon.

The design—like all good designs—follows intent. Many things are defined by their limitations. Desert Rain's limiting factor, implicit in its name, is water: Bend receives an average of just over eleven inches of precipitation per year. The building's ample roof area reflects the challenge of harvesting (and storing) all water needed for all buildings on-site, while the roof pitches angle strategically to capture as much solar energy as possible. The east-west orientation of the main house with its large overhangs remind the visitor of the region's harsh, dry summers and cold winters, while the stucco and concrete function much like massive rocks that hold and slowly release heat.

Like the materials, much of the creativity, intelligence, labor and craftsmanship that went into Desert Rain were also sourced locally or regionally. Desert Rain is a collection of buildings, but it was (and is) also a practical laboratory, providing opportunities to try out new techniques and materials, as well as to test and challenge current regulatory codes. The constructed wetland, for example, designed to process greywater from all three buildings, represents a fundamental departure from how waste is treated in more urban environments. Obtaining approval required hours of research, onerous paperwork and recurring dialogue. The owners

Homeowner Barb Scott talks to a small group touring the Desert Rain site.

and the design team acknowledge that some things could have been done differently, more cost-effectively—arguably, better—but that is the nature of experiments: To test. To observe. To learn.

Desert Rain is also a community. Barb Scott and Tom Elliott initiated the project and kept the momentum up, stoking the fire with their enthusiasm, and just as the project could not have happened without their determined vision and resources, so too it could not have happened without hundreds of talented and committed individuals: the core team, comprised of the designers, general contractor, landscape designers, water systems engineer and sustainability consultant, as well as the many subcontractors and craftspeople who contributed their specific skills. Consultants from near and far lent their expertise, and representatives of municipal and state agencies met with the team to hammer out code issues. Suppliers and vendors worked with the team on materials selection and vetting. Finally, hundreds of people, including schoolchildren, family, friends, residents of Bend and people who were simply curious or craving a dose of inspiration have toured the project in various stages of construction.

Scott and Elliott will continue to host tours and house visiting guests, because their intention is to have Desert Rain function perpetually as a community, laboratory and classroom, even after the project is fully certified as a Living Building. An extensive monitoring system gathers data on the freshwater distribution, power generation and usage, composting system and more, in hopes of informing other Living Building Challenge projects, and other projects that hope to adopt aspects of the Challenge. Desert Rain is a legacy. Though privately owned, the intellectual property is to be held in public trust.

When cataloging Desert Rain's features and all that the project has achieved, it is tempting to gloss over the messy loose ends, frustrations, obstacles that felt like brick walls, endless details, and the care that went into every aspect of the project—in short, the humanity—that went into its making. That would be a grave mistake. Desert Rain is a story, and for humanity, stories hold the power to teach, to move, and to change. Turn the page, and learn how this tale began.

13

At their peak, Bend's lumber mills processed over 500 million board feet a year.

# BEND, OREGON: GROWTH—AND OPPORTUNITY

**The Desert Rain House is located in Oregon's High Desert. With an annual rainfall of 11.4 inches, the region more technically qualifies as scrubland or steppe, but the romantic name has stuck, and understandably so. This landscape, flanked by the Cascade Mountains to the west, is starkly beautiful, spare and lonely and wild, home to herds of pronghorn and elk, and hardscrabble plants like juniper and sagebrush.**

It is not an easy place in which to live. At an average elevation of 4000 feet above sea level, the five-county region is characterized by unrelenting sun in the summer, bitter cold in the winter and huge diurnal temperature swings. (At the Western edge of the High Desert, Bend's elevation is 3,623 feet.) There is very little natural shelter from the elements. Though fine for Ponderosa Pine and sagebrush, the environment has kept the human population in check. Most of the region's towns remain small. By contrast, Bend, population 80,000, is the fifth fastest-growing metropolitan area in the country, according to the 2005 U.S. Census. By 2020, the population within the city's Urban Growth Boundary is projected to reach 100,646, and the total population for the entire Deschutes County will exceed 210,000.

At the turn of the 19th Century, Bend was barely a settlement along the banks of the Deschutes River. By the 1920s, it was a bustling timber town. For the last several decades, alpine skiing, mountain biking, rock climbing and some of the best fly fishing in the state have been attracting a new kind of pioneer. Transitioning from timber to tourism helped Bend escape the hard fate suffered by so many of the state's rural communities. Today, breweries have replaced mills; Mirror Pond Ale is the perfect metaphor, taking its name from the mill pond built in the early 1900s.

"Bend is a mini-version of Marin County [California]," says Desert Rain builder Jim Fagan, who moved from Marin to Bend in the late 1990s. "It's a fairly isolated, stable real estate market; there's always demand."

The Shevlin Commons and Northwest Crossing developments in Bend incorporate many elements of Smart Growth, including walking paths, traffic-calming roundabouts, and preservation of native landscaping.

The ability to work remotely allows more and more people to have their cake and eat it too: professionals can keep their urban-centered jobs and relocate to a place where they can raise children and enjoy less-frenzied, healthier lifestyles. Once those "refugees" settle in, they recruit friends and family to join them, in a self-perpetuating cycle. Baby Boomers nearing retirement are finding Bend ideal, too—a safe place with excellent services, but also with enough cultural and physical stimulation to keep minds and bodies spry.

Other national trends—positive and negative—are playing out on this unlikely High Desert stage.

"Some production builders are going as fast as they possibly can," says Al Tozer of Tozer Design. Some of these companies were temporarily sidelined by the recent Recession, which lasted from late 2007 through the middle of 2009, but they are now accelerating construction in its wake, hoping to cash in on Bend's rapid growth. In 2010, the City sought approval to expand its urban growth boundary by 8400 acres but was denied by Oregon's Land Conservation and Development Commission. A task force is looking at ways to use existing land more efficiently, and it will likely ask for a more modest expansion within the next few years.

On the other hand, Bend has been lauded for embracing the development principles of Smart Growth: promoting pedestrian- and bike-friendly streets and neighborhoods; instituting traffic calming measures like traffic circles and planted medians; planning and revitalizing neighborhoods with "mixed uses"—nodes of commercial activity within residential blocks. And along with scattered "green" projects, there are also a few notable subdivisions that exhibit thoughtful, long-range planning and a commitment to sustainability. For example, Shevlin Commons is a 67-acre development that granted over half its land area as a conservation easement and includes wildlife corridors and pedestrian trails. Many of the custom-built homes meet or exceed Energy Star standards, incorporate local materials and are designed and sited to integrate into the landscape.

What will become of Bend is yet to be determined. Certainly there are signs that the city will choose thoughtful, sustainable development over greed-fueled, unchecked growth. In this context, a project like Desert Rain not only contributes to the conversation, but also ups the ante, challenging assumptions about what truly regenerative, resilient building can look like—today.

15

# WHY WE NEED LIVING BUILDINGS

If you are reading this book, you are probably interested in "green" or sustainable building. You may be familiar with some of the positive trends cropping up all over the country, from the "tiny house" movement to the rise in net zero energy homes to the mainstreaming of certification programs like LEED, Earth Advantage and Passive House. Standard building energy codes have grown more stringent, too, especially in recent years. For example, a house built to the 2009 International Energy Conservation Code (IECC) standards, which many states have adopted, is 30 percent more energy efficient than one built to the 2006

*The Living Building Challenge was developed with a full recognition that there must be an immediate and radical change to the present societal approach to building and to living. Through an uncompromising set of Imperatives, the Living Building Challenge adopts the metaphor of a flower and lays out a beautiful vision of "Living Buildings" — structures that nurture, participate and integrate rather than extract, detract and isolate.*

IECC. The 2012 IECC goes further still, so that a home built to its standards will be 50 percent more efficient than one built to the 2006 code. The growth curve on renewable energy is finally starting to steepen as well; in 2013, solar installations in the United States increased by 41 percent over the previous year.

As encouraging as these signs are, there are equally troubling trends. Climate change threatens health and livelihoods across the globe, exposes millions to devastating storms and flooding and raises uncertainty over food security. In this country, the gap between rich and poor continues to widen. The burden of debt grows even as job opportunities narrow. Health epidemics such as obesity, diabetes and autism are reaching crisis levels. Meanwhile, the plundering of resources and reliance on fossil fuels continues, and habitat loss threatens one-fourth of all known animal species with extinction.

The conventional approach to creating buildings reflects other deep imbalances in our society. Just as the industrialization of agriculture has created a disconnect between ourselves and the food that nurtures us, introduced toxins into our bodies and the environment, and removed us from the impacts of growing and raising our food, so too has the industrialization of building construction created a disconnect between ourselves and our buildings. This building industrialism has alienated the vast majority of people from the resources required to build, operate and maintain buildings of all types. Buildings, including our houses, have become repositories of toxic materials and products.

Futhermore, this building industrialism has brought about the standardization of materials and processes that has too often compromised the craft of building. At its worst, production building imposes generic designs on landscapes that disregard local and regional climate, geography and

history. Subdivisions separate homes from jobs, markets and schools, and isolate them with busy roads that discourage walking or bicycling. Structures are built for bottom-line profits, not longevity, using sub-par and, in some cases, toxic materials and construction methods that favor size over quality, generating waste and resulting in "buildings on life support." Such buildings depend on fossil fuel energy and water that itself requires large amounts of energy to process and transport, and they generate wastewater that is carried long distances to treat with more chemicals and more energy.

Fortunately, there are builders, developers, architects, homeowners, government officials and activists all across the country who are refuting and opposing these disastrous conventions. As a result there are some positive changes related to the building industry that are occurring, albeit in some regions more quickly than others. The Pacific Northwest is recognized as a leader in this regard. However, much work remains to tip the scales toward broad-scale sustainable development.

The Living Building Challenge was developed with full recognition of the urgent need to radically change the current approach to building. Through an uncompromising set of Imperatives, the Living Building Challenge adopts the metaphor of a flower and lays out a beautiful vision of "Living Buildings" — structures that nurture, participate and integrate rather than extract, detract and isolate.

"We believe that everything is connected. Nothing happens from a single cause, no action generates a single effect, or has a unique meaning, writes Tom Elliott on the subject of sustainability. "This is the web of life, but we feel it also pertains more and more to human institutions." This includes the human-built environment.

17

# THE MOST RADICAL GREEN BUILDING PROGRAM ON THE PLANET

The Living Building Challenge shares aspects with other green building certification programs, but differs in several fundamental ways. First, under the Challenge, buildings earn certification based on actual, not modeled, performance, as verified through twelve consecutive months of performance data. Second, the Living Building Challenge is not prescriptive. Buildings must meet all twenty Imperatives, but project teams can choose how to achieve them. This self-determination aspect acknowledges the uniqueness of each project, and allows for regional, local and site-specific solutions.

Following the flower metaphor, the twenty Imperatives are arranged within seven Petal categories. To achieve full certification, projects must meet all relevant Imperatives within all seven Petals. The Living Building Challenge Standard is a fluid document. Already in its fifth iteration, the Imperatives change to adapt to changing circumstances tied to evolving building codes, available technologies and product innovations. Desert Rain was registered under Living Building Challenge Version 2.1.

**LIVING BUILDING CHALLENGE**

## SITE: RESTORING A HEALTHY COEXISTENCE WITH NATURE

**INTENT:** To identify where it is acceptable to build, how to care for a site once it is developed, and to cultivate self-sufficient, pedestrian-oriented communities.

01: LIMITS TO GROWTH
02: URBAN AGRICULTURE
03: HABITAT EXCHANGE
04: CAR-FREE LIVING

## WATER: CREATING WATER INDEPENDENT SITES, BUILDINGS AND COMMUNITIES

**INTENT:** To respect clean freshwater as the precious resource that it is, through thoughtful use and on-site management.

05: NET ZERO WATER
06: ECOLOGICAL WATER FLOW

## ENERGY: RELYING ONLY ON CURRENT SOLAR INCOME

**INTENT:** To create buildings that only rely on non-polluting, renewable forms of energy.

07: NET ZERO ENERGY

## HEALTH: MAXIMIZING PHYSICAL AND PSYCHOLOGICAL HEALTH AND WELL-BEING

**INTENT:** To address all the conditions which contribute to the creation of nourishing, healthy indoor spaces.

08: CIVILIZED ENVIRONMENT
09: HEALTHY AIR
10: BIOPHILIA

## MATERIALS: ENDORSING PRODUCTS AND PROCESSES THAT ARE SAFE FOR ALL SPECIES THROUGH TIME

**INTENT:** To induce a successful "materials economy" that is non-toxic, transparent and socially equitable.

11: RED LIST
12: EMBODIED CARBON FOOTPRINT
13: RESPONSIBLE INDUSTRY
14: APPROPRIATE SOURCING
15: CONSERVATION + REUSE

## EQUITY: SUPPORTING A JUST, EQUITABLE WORLD

**INTENT:** To align development and the design of our buildings to promote human dignity, equality and a true sense of community.

16: HUMAN SCALE + HUMANE PLACES
17: DEMOCRACY + SOCIAL JUSTICE
18: RIGHTS TO NATURE

## BEAUTY: CELEBRATING DESIGN THAT CREATES TRANSFORMATIVE CHANGE

**INTENT:** To recognize the role beauty plays in prompting people to care for and conserve their environments.

19: BEAUTY + SPIRIT
20: INSPIRATION + EDUCATION

These Imperatives constituted the "tall order" faced by the Desert Rain team. Furthermore, it is vitally important to understand that the Living Building Challenge is not just a green building certification program. "It's also an advocacy tool used to create change, to identify where the barriers are," says ML Vidas, architect and Living Building Challenge Ambassador. "Finally, it's a philosophy; that is the part that grabs our hearts."

# PART II

*People*

Modern Pioneers
Pursuing a Bold Vision

21

DESERT RAIN HOUSE

*"If one of our real concerns is with sustainable quality of life for all people—if this is our design assignment—then we have to penetrate the economic myths embedded in our culture, free ourselves from the obsession with growth and consumption, and dramatically refocus our economic relationships in order to accomplish it."*

**TOM ELLIOTT**, on sustainability lessons learned

# STORY AND THE SEEDS OF DESERT RAIN

**To date, most projects striving to meet the rigorous standards of the Living Building Challenge have been public buildings—schools, education centers, and the like. Although there are more every day, residential projects have been scarcer, and for good reason. Living Building Challenge projects demand a tremendous dedication of time and resources—financial and otherwise. There are many unknowns and even more obstacles.**

Mary Louise (ML) Vidas, architect and Living Building Challenge Ambassador who served as the sustainability consultant for Desert Rain, often calls Tom Elliott and Barbara Scott "true modern pioneers."

"Think about pioneers in the 1830s and 1840s, heading west," she says. "They said goodbye to family and friends, loaded up the wagon and start heading across the Great Plains. People thought they were crazy." Just as those pioneers overcame incredible obstacles, making the path easier for those who followed in their footsteps, so will pioneering projects smooth the way for subsequent Living Building Challenge teams.

Together, Elliott and Scott had the financial resources to take on a project as ambitious as Desert Rain. But taking on the Living Building Challenge required more than money. What about those key ingredients: motivation and confidence? What made them want to do it? What made them think they could?

Many landmark moments led Elliott and Scott to embrace the Living Building Challenge. Understanding their personal journeys—both as individuals and as a couple—may hold keys for hastening the spread of the Living Building Challenge, and the sustainability movement in general.

23

# LESSONS FROM THE N-BAR: TOM'S STORY

Tom Elliott grew up in Roswell, New Mexico, the son of a well-established family invested in oil and gas exploration and ranching.

He received a strict formal military education at the New Mexico Military Institute, but spent summers on his grandfather's ranch in Montana: the N-Bar, a 48,000-acre spread with a reputation for producing quality Angus cattle. Tom loved the demanding physical labor, and found he had a knack for trouble-shooting farm machinery.

Tom recalls being attracted to "alternative" ways of thinking at a young age, even as he upheld family traditions.

"My way of getting around the oppressive military culture was to excel at it, so I had more choices," he says.

After earning his MBA at Duke University, Tom decided to join the family business. He found himself spending more and more time at the N-Bar, and by 1978 he had taken over its management.

"This time in agriculture was the height of applied inputs and faith in the supremacy of technology," says Tom. Some hard lessons forced him to rethink the economic and ecologic wisdom of relying on outside inputs and managing for single outcomes. One episode—a failed attempt to eradicate an invasive plant called leafy spurge with heavy, repeated applications of herbicide—prompted him to completely change his management approach (see sidebar on pages 28-29).

"The ranch became my little symphony of sorts," says Tom. Informed by his inquiry into complexity science, he began diversifying, introducing sheep and rotational grazing and experimenting with organic agriculture and woodland restoration. He implemented a "flat" management style and changed his approach to cattle breeding: rather than selecting solely for large size and fast growth, he began breeding for a suite of traits, including such things as cows' mothering and milking ability. The N-Bar produced many stellar bulls and cows, including a Black Angus bull that became the most widely used sire in the history of the breed.

Of course, Tom was not doing this work alone. Several families worked the ranch, forming a community Tom came to care for deeply. The ranch continued to flower into the 1990s, attracting everyone from foreign dignitaries to idealistic young interns and colleagues in the industry, hoping to learn from the N-Bar's progressive practices. Tom also traveled the country, delivering keynote addresses and consulting with other ranchers.

24

"The ranch became a touchstone for a lot of people in the early days of sustainable agriculture," he says.

When Tom's father died in 1996, ownership of the N-Bar fell into the hands of Tom and his two siblings. At that time, the ranch was not performing well financially, in part because of fluctuations inherent to the industry, but also because some of Tom's experiments did not yield short-term profits. His brother and sister wanted to sell.

"It was a three-way vote, and I lost," says Tom. "But partly because of my own arrogance and inability to communicate effectively [about the ranch operations] to family members, other than my father."

The sale of the ranch was heartbreaking. But Tom realized he could either lose himself in bitterness or learn from the experience.

"I knew I wanted to take the knowledge gained there and do something more enlivening with it." He was also searching for something that had eluded him his entire life: home. Despite his successes with the ranch community, Tom's personal life, particularly his previous two marriages, had been marked by chaos and transience. His three daughters, Sarah, Alisa and Kate, were grown and living their own lives. He was ready to put down roots.

25

# MOUNTAINS AND OBSTACLES: BARB'S STORY

**While Tom Elliott came from a background where hard work, discipline and academic excellence were expected, Barbara Scott's childhood was much less structured. Her family moved from the East Coast to Boulder, Colorado when she was seven, sparking a lifelong love affair with the mountains.**

Although her parents shared her passion for camping, both her mother and father came from large families where education was considered a luxury, and they were not able to lend much support in that area. Barb barely graduated high school and left home the day after graduation, working at restaurants and at odd jobs in several states.

Barb realized these service jobs were not the ticket to improving her life. She decided to return to school. She moved to Arizona to study midwifery, but the school folded. Once she moved to Montana she became interested in home economics.

"I was attracted to the broad base of studies under that umbrella—budgeting, cooking, nutrition, psychology, child development, family life, work/life balance," says Barb. She was taking classes at Montana State University when she became pregnant. She knew she did not want to spend the rest of her life with the baby's father, but decided to keep the baby. Her daughter Lily was born in June of 1984.

"She totally changed my life for the better," says Barb. Still, she was a single mother without a degree and no family nearby to help. She was just about to launch a business— an environmentally-friendly cloth diaper service— when a fire destroyed the bar that supplied her trailer with water and power (see sidebar on pages 30-31).

"That was one of the low points of my life," says Barb. She had to abandon her business plan, but with support from friends, tutors and the local social services agency, she started

climbing out of poverty. She found Section 8 housing, earned a degree in education and began teaching. Her first job was on the Crow Indian reservation. Subsequent jobs took her back to the East Coast, then to Bend, Oregon, when Lily was seven. Back in her beloved mountains, Barb finally began to put down roots, working for school districts and eventually earning a Masters in Special Education from Lewis and Clark College. Many of her jobs before and since have involved helping students launch businesses and manage their finances.

"I've been in poverty," Barb explains. "At various times I've wanted to work with single mothers and help them be resourceful, because I didn't have any help."

With Lily in college, Barb accepted an administrative position in Montana. It was there that she met Tom Elliott.

# CONFLUENCE:
# A MEETING OF MINDS AND SPIRITS

**When Tom and Barb met, Tom was detangling from a divorce and regrouping after the sale of the N-Bar. Despite their contrasting backgrounds, they found much common ground, including a love of opera and the outdoors.**

Barb had never let her difficult financial circumstances keep her from adventuring; she had always carved out time for camping, hiking, cycling, rafting and skiing, whether with Lily or with friends. Now she and Tom began creating new adventures together, including a two-and-a-half-month bicycle trip that began on the Oregon Coast and ended with dipping their bicycle tires in the Atlantic Ocean.

The couple settled into an old renovated farmhouse outside of Livingston, Montana, which Barb took over and turned into a successful vacation rental, still thriving today. They began investing in real estate, buying rentals and building new homes. Though they designed these spec homes to match the historic character of downtown Livingston, there was nothing unconventional about their construction; they didn't even think about "building green."

After Tom and Barb married, they agreed they needed to leave Montana to make a fresh start as a couple. They relocated to Bend.

"It was a difficult time," Barb admits. "I had all these friends who remembered me as a single mom. Now I was back, with a diamond ring on my finger and a new husband." At the same time, she and Tom were excited about doing a project together—they just did not know exactly what.

As they searched for a permanent home, their realtor began showing them large ridgetop "trophy houses" with panoramic views. Although Barb could not picture herself living in such a house, she admits the image was somewhat seductive.

"It was a good time to look at my values and ask, what do I want?" One day, while riding her bicycle, Barb happened by a lot for sale. She stopped. In contrast to the exclusive neighborhoods the realtor was showing them, this property was in an old section in the heart of downtown, with modest homes and welcoming alleyways. She immediately called their realtor. Later, she found out the adjacent lot was for sale as well.

"Barb was attracted to this area because of the funky, small mill houses, whereas my vision tended to be more grandiose," Tom says. He admits that without Barb—despite his experiments in sustainable ranching at the N-Bar, and despite his broad knowledge and interest in "green" technologies—he probably would have put some solar panels on top of an existing house and called it good. Still, when Barb called from the top of a mountain, breathless from snow-shoeing, and declared she was ready to buy the downtown lots, Tom agreed.

"I was terrified about committing, but also excited," he says. But once they decided to build rather than buy, they never looked back. Tom and Barb finally had a new project they could sink their teeth into, and they began drafting a list of requirements for what was to be their über-green house. Both were looking forward to creating something that others could learn and benefit from. They did not know it, but they were about to enter uncharted territory.

"It's difficult to comprehend the expense, the difficulty of what Tom and Barb have done," says Mary Louise, "They didn't risk their lives, but they have put their resources and reputations on the line."

Tom and Barb were motivated by very different personal experiences to create something larger than themselves, with the potential for legacy. They had reached the point in their "sustainability journeys" that made them receptive and confident. What they needed now was a stellar team to turn their vision into reality.

# TOM ELLIOTT VERSUS THE LEAFY SPURGE

**Thirty years ago something happened that changed the course of my life forever. It was not a singular event, but rather a gradual accumulation of experience that resulted in an epiphany.**

At the time I was partner and manager of a large 48,000-acre Montana ranching operation known as the N-Bar Ranch. While an extraordinarily diverse and beautiful landscape, the ranch suffered from one serious blemish— many acres of the operation had been invaded by an infestation of a noxious weed known as leafy spurge.

As a young ranch manager, I considered this plant an affront to my ability to manage the landscape effectively. Consequently, I approached a well-known multi-national chemical company for herbicide recommendations to control this invasive species. This company was so confident their top-of-the-line herbicide would eradicate the weed they proffered a wager. The exact terms of the wager are lost to me now, but the criteria for winning or losing involved a study conducted by a graduate student at Montana State University. The chemical company wagered the herbicide application would kill the spurge and thereby at least double the biomass available to my cattle as

Armed with $25,000 worth of herbicide, I launched a massive effort to eradicate the leafy spurge. In the spring of 1982, I anxiously awaited the greening of the hillsides to measure the effects of my efforts. Sadly, while more sparse, the spurge still occupied the same acreage or more.

With great determination and laser focus, the chemical company and I determined that a second application would be required. We mounted a campaign from land and air to ensure our success and retired from the battle to await the next spring so we could measure our success.

During the interim summer, I noticed a number of dying ponderosa pines in forestlands adjacent to the sprayed areas and my cattle suffered an odd epidemic of brisket edema, a pulmonary disorder. While assured by the chemical company that there was no possible connection, I was disconcerted.

Meanwhile, my graduate student's study revealed that, not only had the spraying failed to double the grass production, it had actually reduced the total available biomass by killing all the smaller forbs that grow in community with range grasses. (Interestingly, fifteen years later these test plots still had not recovered to their original levels of productivity.)

Concerned, I decided to tour the company's showplace ranch in Wyoming where they claimed to have eradicated leafy spurge. What I found was appalling—the ranch looked like a war zone with skeletal remains of trees, no brush, weak yellowed grass and a few hardy spurge plants. Come to think of it, the rancher didn't look so healthy either.

On the tour, the company representative proudly proclaimed that the herbicide control would have a long-term effect because the active chemical persisted in the soil for up to five years.

My epiphany came when I realized the company rep and I were looking at the same landscape and seeing diametrically opposed images. He saw single-minded "success." I was shocked: the "unintended consequences" of the accepted control method resulted in cataclysmic damage to the underlying natural system.

In that moment the realization dawned on me that you cannot isolate one aspect of life from another. In my ignorance, I had been trying to surgically remove a single plant species from a complex, inter-related life system in order to restore my sense of order and harmony. And I was operating from the narrow perspective of a stockman—if a cow couldn't eat it, the plant was worthless and taking up precious space in my rangeland.

I began to think more broadly and creatively about my relationship with leafy spurge. In 1984, I partnered with a neighboring sheep producer to study the possible effects of grazing sheep on leafy spurge. Common wisdom at the time was the plant was toxic to sheep and would likely kill them. Imagine our surprise when the sheep not only prospered on the plant, but actually seemed to prefer it!

By 1986 we had increased our cooperative sheep grazing effort to include three thousand sheep. By adding complexity and cooperation to the system, we were able to turn more solar energy into useable protein for humans, eliminate a huge expenditure, increase our income, and deepen our sense of community throughout.

29

# EAT BEAR:
# USING STORY TO INSPIRE OTHERS

**In 2012, Barbara Scott started a website called Eat Bear: a story-sharing forum where people can post stories of overcoming challenge, whether health, financial, or interpersonal in nature. The site is not reserved for writers, says Scott; anyone with a story can contribute.**

"It's about facing your fears and living your passion," says Scott. "Some days you're going to eat bear; other days the bear's gonna eat you."

This is Barbara Scott's Eat Bear story.

I was 26, on my own with little Lily, and trying to finish college. I was sure I wanted to be home with Lily during the beginning of her life, as well as make a life for us—all on a very low, government-subsidized income. I had no family support in the town where I lived. I babysat along with receiving welfare checks, and saved enough money to put a down payment on a very old trailer located on private land outside of Bozeman, Montana. This was in the country, not in a trailer park.

I wanted to open an environmentally-friendly cloth diaper service. I researched the business idea and came up with its name: "A Change for the Better." The start-up costs were minimal. I had a small truck, a home with a washer and dryer and more than anything, I was motivated. I was ready to purchase supplies and open my doors.

On the night of January 5, 1985, there was a fire in the bar that supplied power to my trailer. From that night on, I had no power in my home. The bank would not let me stop payments while I rented a place in town and either sold or moved my trailer, which meant I was facing a wicked Montana winter with a baby under the age of one. The only way I was able to stay was because I had a woodstove and qualified for free wood—and because of a deep willpower, which still serves me today. We made it through the winter with Bozeman Hot Springs a couple of miles away for baths, buckets of water from the gas station to flush the toilet, my little Coleman stove to cook on and great friends to hold me up.

The following spring, I was riding my bike around Bozeman and happened through one of those old "grandfathered-in" trailer parks, where I spotted a vacant lot. The short of it was I was able to move my trailer there, with the help of a friend who believed in me and lent me the money.

I started renting the trailer, returned to school and started saving money. I eventually sold the trailer for a profit, which allowed me to put a down payment on my home in Tumalo, Oregon six years later.

After I moved to Bend, one of my first positions in the schools was working with junior and senior high school students with mild learning disabilities. These are students who often fall through the cracks of our education system and I was determined to give them a better educational experience and sense of purpose.

We needed a place to meet. I learned of a house that was going to be torn down, so I arranged to have it moved onto the school campus, organized my students, and we gutted and renovated that building. It is still being used today.

My spirit is an "Eat Bear" spirit, and I relied on it many times during the designing and building of Desert Rain. Often, when some aspect of the project was stalled or off track, I would step in and say, 'We need to address this; we need to talk about this.' It wasn't easy, but I was willing to take on that role. There was never any doubt in my mind that we could do it—that we could build this Living Building, even when I sensed others were ready to give up.

"*Barb is the heart and soul of Desert Rain. Her sense of adventure, creativity in the face of adversity, and strong bias for action informed the process of designing and building from the beginning. She was the one with the courage to address conflict and bring light to difficult interpersonal concerns that are part and parcel in any human endeavor.*"

**TOM ELLIOTT**

# TALENT AND PASSION: THE DESERT RAIN TEAM

**In the fall of 2008, Elliott and Scott hired friend and construction consultant Karen Benson to help them draft a Request for Proposals (RFP) to prospective architects and designers. Attached to the RFP was the couple's ambitious "sustainability agenda," which included thirteen specific objectives and a number of criteria describing their aesthetic, which Elliott and Scott defined as "neo-funk." They were also toying with LEED certification but they had not committed to the program yet.**

Even then the couple knew they wanted to build a residential compound, consisting of one new structure and an extensive remodel of one of the existing mill houses. The compound was to be largely energy independent, maximize the connections between inside and outside spaces, incorporate recycled and reclaimed materials, and capture rainwater and utilize greywater. They were well on their way to anticipating the Living Building Challenge agenda before they knew it existed.

By January of 2009, Benson had helped them identify several prospective architecture and design firms.

"We'd never done this before, so Karen [Benson] suggested we invite everyone to the site for a group interview," says Scott. On an unseasonably warm day in late January, a group of architects and designers assembled at the Shasta Place property. Scott and Elliott introduced themselves, explained their vision, read through their design criteria and answered questions in front of a clearly uncomfortable group. The architects and designers, all of whom knew each other, were put in the awkward position of asking potential clients questions that would normally be kept confidential.

"It was awkward," Elliott admits, "but at the same time we were hoping it would sort out those who were curious and creative enough to go through the effort of submitting a proposal." The open-ended meeting also set the tone of the project: unconventional, and committed to transparency.

Some expressed skepticism about Scott and Elliott's ability to see a project of such magnitude through, but ultimately four firms submitted proposals.

Though all submissions had their merits, the proposal from Tozer Design stood out. With nineteen years' experience in sustainable design, the firm was ahead of the curve; the City of Bend had created a special award for Outstanding Environmentally Sensitive Residence for one of their projects in 1996. Principal Al Tozer's credentials included a background in biology and ecology, which informed his design approach. But more than that, it was his irrepressible enthusiasm for the Desert Rain project and clear alignment with Elliott and Scott's goals that made him best suited for the project.

"Everything changed when we met Al," says Scott. "He's an artist; he asks great questions and was just so excited."

Al Tozer's support staff included architectural designer Cecile Cuddihy, who helped develop the design and provided conceptual designs, and Sarah Currier, who served as both interior designer and project manager. Later on, when Sarah took a leave of absence from Tozer Design, interior designer Wendy Knight took over her duties.

After settling on a design firm, Elliott and Scott sent out an RFP to builders, some of whom Al Tozer had recommended. They interviewed several—individually, this time—and toured their projects. One of the firms was Timberline Construction, custom homebuilders with a strong resume of "green" projects and experience with alternative construction methods, including Insulated Concrete Forms (ICFs) and straw bale. Timberline formed out of a partnership between James (Jim) Fagan and Kristian Willman. Fagan had cut his teeth in Marin County, California in the 1980s, building high-end custom homes for some of the higher profile architects in the area; Willman had owned roofing and framing companies and worked as a project manager for a well-established developer in the Bend area.

"WE HAVE REVIEWED YOUR EARLY DESIGN CRITERIA NOTES AND HAVE FOUND YOUR CONTEMPORARY NORTHWEST "GREEN GOALS" INSPIRING, FUN AND AN IDEAL MATCH TO OUR OWN SUSTAINABLE MISSION. WE ESPECIALLY APPRECIATE YOUR SUGGESTIONS OF AN ECLECTIC APPROACH TO FINISH DETAILS AND YOUR ENCOURAGEMENT OF SURPRISE AS A CREATIVE DESIGN PROGRAM COMPONENT."

QUOTE FROM TOZER DESIGN'S PROPOSAL

The Desert Rain team:
(top) Chris Hart-Henderson, James Fagan, Al Tozer, Morgan Brown, Kristian Willman, and John Grove
(bottom) Bruce Sullivan, ML Vidas, Ani Cahill, Tom Elliott, and Barb Scott

33

Scott and Elliott had been introduced to Jim Fagan months before embarking on the search for a contractor, and the builder had been "consistently persistent" about his desire to be a part of the Desert Rain project. The couple felt Fagan's experience with progressive building techniques, along with his laid-back demeanor, made him a good candidate to serve as Desert Rain's general contractor. As with Al Tozer's proposal, it was Timberline's enthusiasm and willingness to work collaboratively on a team as much as the company's experience that convinced Scott and Elliott to hire the firm.

Timberline had never worked with Tozer Design before. "It took some time for Al Tozer to trust us," admits Fagan. "But in the end he was very comfortable with how we make decisions. We really try to deliver the designer's intent, rather than make assumptions."

Elliott and Scott hired Timberline in June of 2009. By then Heart Springs Landscape Design had also joined team Desert Rain. Heart Springs owner Chris Hart-Henderson claims over twenty years' experience with sustainable landscape design, using plants native to Central Oregon and including rainwater harvesting and stormwater management. Her staff includes landscape designer Ani Cahill. Early on, the two met with Al and Cecile to discuss placement of the house, the indoor-outdoor relationships and the merits of the existing trees and plants.

Late in the summer Elliott and Scott made the decision to go for LEED Platinum certification. They realized they were going to need someone to help guide them through the process, and they found just the right person in Mary Louise (ML) Vidas. Vidas had made a mid-life career change from artist to architect and was completing the necessary internships to become fully licensed; in fact, she had been present at the initial "group interview" with Neal Huston and Associates Architects. Vidas was also in the process of becoming a Living Building Challenge

"ON EVERY CONSTRUCTION PROJECT THERE ARE A VARIETY OF VOICES, EACH WITH HIS/HER OWN GOALS AND VIEWPOINT. WE VALUE YOUR DECISION TO INVOLVE YOUR BUILDER DURING THE DESIGN PROCESS AND ARE WILLING TO TAKE AN ACTIVE ROLE. SIMILARLY, WE EMBRACE THE INVOLVEMENT OF DESIGNERS DURING THE CONSTRUCTION PHASE OF OUR PROJECTS. THIS CONTINUAL COLLABORATION RESULTS IN A BALANCE BETWEEN THOUGHTFUL DESIGN AND PRACTICAL IMPLEMENTATION."

QUOTE FROM TIMBERLINE PROPOSAL

Ambassador, and would later join the board of the Cascadia Green Building Council. Articulate, meticulous, passionate but calm, she was the ideal person to take the project through the LEED certification process—and later, to play a vital role guiding the team through the Living Building Challenge, particularly in the arduous task of vetting materials.

Another key member of the team, Morgan Brown of Whole Water Systems, did not join the Desert Rain team until April of 2010, soon after the decision to commit to the Living Building Challenge. Whole Water Systems specializes in holistic approaches to water management for both commercial and residential projects, including rainwater catchment, greywater systems and the use of "Constructed Wetland Bioreactors," or CWBs.

Scott's background in education and experience leading ambitious group projects was key to fostering a creative, collaborative atmosphere.

*"By nature, design by committee is not efficient, in terms of time. But it is highly effective."*

TOM ELLIOTT

# GETTING DOWN TO BUSINESS

**By the fall of 2009, the core team of Tozer Design, Timberline Construction, Heart Springs Design and consultant Mary Louise (ML) Vidas were meeting regularly, sometimes at the project site, but just as often, at Elliott and Scott's dining table.**

Integrated design is one of the buzz phrases in sustainable building projects. At its most basic, it means having everyone involved in the process early on; that way, the builder can inform the designer, especially on matters of cost, and the designer can help guide the project once construction begins, ensuring the original intent is preserved and expressed.

Though integrated design is a necessary and common strategy on complicated custom building projects, it is even more imperative on Living Building Challenge projects, which are by their nature breaking new ground.

To take but one example, the orientation and siting of the building affects the existing landscaping and informs the new landscaping

design. It also affects energy efficiency and generation (the effectiveness of passive solar orientation and active solar PV systems, for example) and water management, from the location of cisterns and design of the rainwater collection system to the capture of stormwater flows. Siting impacts the Beauty and Equity Petals by determining a building's accessibility and connection to other structures on the site and on adjacent properties. Such an important decision could not be made by Tozer Design without the input of other team members.

Above all, integrated design requires communication: frequent phone calls, multiple email chains, and most importantly, regular meetings.

"We spent countless hours in Al Tozer's office, and he in ours, all working together," says Willman. "It's a very collaborative process, probably the most people involved that I've ever worked with on one project." For Scott and Elliott, who both came from backgrounds where working collaboratively was key, the team approach came naturally.

"By nature, design by committee is not efficient, in terms of time," says Elliott. "But it is highly effective."

They were fortunate that Bend, despite its relatively small size, had such a pool of talent and experience from which to draw. All of the core team members, excepting Morgan Brown, lived in the area. Brown, who had personal connections in Bend, was headquartered in Idaho when he first came on board, then moved to Seattle—still close enough to enable several site visits.

37

# A COMMON VISION

As the project progressed, the constellation of subcontractors, vendors and support staff grew. One of the reasons for requiring every person who worked on the project to learn about the Living Building Challenge was to make sure everyone was on the same page, and to ensure each person understood the importance of making certain every product and material brought onto the site had been vetted. As new people joined the project, Vidas, Elliott and Scott gave dozens of one-hour presentations on the Living Building Challenge. Elliott and Fagan developed a Participant Agreement Form which every subcontractor, employee of a subcontractor and volunteer was required to review and sign. The form included sections on materials, particularly the Red List requirements, and expectations around conservation and reuse and workmanship; it also reminded participants that, simply by working on Desert Rain, they had become ambassadors for the Living Building Challenge. Timberline also required all subcontractors to review and sign a form entitled Subcontractor Responsibilities and Expectations.

"Every time we have someone step on-site they need to be educated," says Kristian Willman. "Bottom line, we have to find the right people and they have to buy into the Living Building Challenge. They have to believe it."

*"At first I thought we'd be met with resistance from the subs. Quite the contrary: they were keenly interested in how to make this project succeed, and wanted to see how their contribution fit into the big picture."*

ML VIDAS

Though physical distance is not the barrier it once was, and technology allows virtual conferencing via Skype, regular meetings on-site were invaluable for working out specific problems—and sometimes, for simply venting frustrations.

"There were many instances where Tom and Barb just wanted to share what they were feeling; it wasn't about any particular feature or money," says Tozer. "To be able to share that face to face with the team was very helpful."

Roles were well-defined, and in some cases, expanded. Al Tozer took the lead through the design phase; Jim Fagan took over once construction began. ML Vidas served as the hub for materials vetting. Scott and Elliott's involvement was critical; in addition to participating in the hundreds of decisions, from the color of the countertops to the type and size of the renewable energy system, each brought vital skills to the table. Elliott's technical knowledge and love of research contributed to many of the systems, products and materials incorporated in Desert Rain. Scott upheld the project's vision and cultivated a social atmosphere, which helped people feel connected to both the project and each other. She also looked for opportunities to educate and spread the word about the project.

Not that it was always easy. Although the Desert Rain project was fortunate to have such a rare assemblage of talent and experience, it was the first Living Building Challenge project for all of them, which meant they had to come up with one-off solutions with very little guidance. Almost every team member expressed frustration at the lack of signposts. The integrated design approach and added burden of research and meeting time added significantly to the cost of the project. Virtually every team member had to commit time to educate themselves on various aspects of the Living Building Challenge—and not all of that time was billable.

However, a shared sense of mission drove the Desert Rain team forward— the sense that each was contributing to something larger than themselves, something with the potential to literally change the world.

"Like people attract like team members," says Tozer. "None of us were heavily ego-driven. The team was receptive to hearing both the highs and the lows, and that makes a huge difference."

# LIVING BUILDING CHALLENGE AND DESERT RAIN: PARTICIPANT AGREEMENT FORM

Desert Rain is one of the first single-family residences in the world to attempt certification under the Living Building Challenge (LBC). The Living Building Challenge is the most advanced measure of sustainable construction on the planet today and requires strict adherence and documentation.

As a Participant (any subcontractor, employee of a subcontractor, or volunteer) in this project you agree to attend an orientation session on the LBC and to ensure that you and your team adhere strictly to the LBC guidelines. If you have any question about compliance, you agree to contact Timberline Construction of Bend (TCB) prior to bringing in any materials or performing any work that might jeopardize the project certification.

## MATERIALS

Materials and chemicals listed on the Living Building Challenge's Red List include polyvinyl chloride (PVC), chemically treated wood and halogenated flame retardants.

Specifically, the project cannot contain any of the following Red List materials or chemicals.

- Asbestos
- Cadmium
- Chlorinated Polyethylene and Chlorosulfonated Polyethlene43
- Chlorofluorocarbons (CFCs)
- Chloroprene (Neoprene)
- Formaldehyde (added)
- Halogenated Flame Retardants44
- Hydrochlorofluorocarbons (HCFCs)
- Lead (added)
- Mercury
- Petrochemical Fertilizers and Pesticides45
- Phthalates
- Polyvinyl Chloride (PVC)
- Wood treatments containing Creosote, Arsenic or Pentachlorophenol

Participants are expected to strictly adhere to these requirements. This includes bringing any products containing prohibited materials onto the job site.

## CONSERVATION AND REUSE:

During construction, teams must divert wasted material from landfills to the following levels:

## MATERIAL MINIMUM DIVERTED/WEIGHT:

Metals: 95%

Paper & Cardboard: 95%

Soil and Biomass: 100%

Rigid Foam, Carpet & Insulation: 90%

All others – combined weighted average: 80%

TCB will provide a material conservation management plan that explains how the construction job site will handle materials to ensure compliance with these requirements. All Participants must adhere carefully to that plan.

## WORKMANSHIP:

TCB has specified their Workmanship Policy above. In addition, please know that your workmanship will be viewed by building professionals throughout the U.S. and internationally. Participation in the construction of Desert Rain will showcase your work—you've been selected for this project because you are among the elite in your particular area of focus. Please ensure any work performed meets the highest possible levels of care and craftsmanship.

## PROFESSIONALISM AND PUBLIC RELATIONS:

Due to the unusual nature of this project, the construction site may experience a wide variety of visitors. As a participant, you are an ambassador for the Desert Rain house and Living Building Challenge. You are expected to understand the basics of the LBC and to be able to represent TCB, Desert Rain and the LBC in a positive and professional manner at all times.

By signing below, you agree that you have read the above information and agree to LBC/Desert Rain guidelines:

_____     _____
Signature                    Date

_____
Printed Name

*"Regarding Size: It's not about a 2999 square foot house. To me, it's about a home I love, find comfortable, and feel proud to share as a lighter footprint on the earth—and that means a smaller home. We realize an email exchange occurred in which we suggested a 4000 square foot home as a target. As the project evolves, however, we find ourselves wanting to challenge ourselves and our team to live in less space. Can we put that number behind us and work with 2500-2800 square feet as a goal for the primary residence?"*

**NOTE FROM BARB SCOTT TO AL TOZER, JUNE 28, 2009**

# EVOLUTION: FROM GREEN DESIGN TO LIVING BUILDING

By fall of 2009, Tozer Design had completed initial design of Desert Rain I, which featured a two-story main residence, detached garage with a living "green" roof, and an Accessory Dwelling Unit above a second garage. Scott and Elliott loved it, but requested the process be "slowed down" in order to better evaluate systems, green building options and revisit the site plan with the intention of balancing tree preservation with solar access. Still, they hoped to submit construction documents by early spring of 2010. Then the couple left on their backpacking trip, where they heard Jason F. McLennan's keynote speech for the Bioneers Conference.

To Scott and Elliott, the Living Building Challenge was "common sense, yet something not yet imagined or articulated."

"Without hesitation, we knew we wanted to do this," says Scott. "We called a meeting and told [the team] what we wanted to do. Without hesitation, they agreed."

By early December 2009 they had officially registered the project with what was then the International Living Building Institute. Though Tozer, Fagan and the rest of the team were enthusiastic about the Living Building Challenge, they didn't realize what they had signed up for.

The Desert Rain team explored many ideas as the project evolved from "deep green" to Living Building.

They did understand that accommodating the Living Building Challenge was going to increase the cost estimate. Though rigorous, LEED standards did not require the home to be net zero energy or to collect and process all water and wastewater on-site. A meeting in early January 2010 included an agenda item to discuss whether to let go of the original design and start anew or to "save" the Living Building Challenge for a future project and concentrate on achieving LEED Gold or Platinum. In the end they decided to "retrofit" the Living Building Challenge into the original design.

Tozer went to work. Everything had to be re-examined, including the purpose and square footage of every room. Tozer proposed several changes to increase the main house's energy efficiency and get the project closer to net zero energy: increasing the thickness of some of the walls from 2 x 8 to 2 x 12, increasing R-values with the use of spray foam insulation and reducing the glazing area from 47 to 37 percent—a 21 percent reduction. Bruce Sullivan of Earth Advantage performed an energy

analysis, based on the area and expected performance of windows and doors and R-values of floors, walls and roofs. All appliances were reevaluated in light of their energy and water consumption. Tozer instructed that all fixtures would have to be WaterSense certified, at minimum; all appliances, Energy Star or better. Meanwhile, Vidas began the overwhelming task of cataloguing and vetting all of the materials for compliance with the Red List and Appropriate Sourcing criteria.

Heart Springs Design calculated a rough water budget, based on the water harvesting capacity of the roofs and average rainfall values. Upon analysis, Hart-Henderson recommended the garage roof be converted from a living "green" roof to a shed roof that could collect rainwater. Scott and Elliott brought Whole Water Systems on board to help with the Water Petal requirements, which were quickly identified as the most challenging. Collecting every drop of rain and snow from the roofs was imperative, but the complicated rooflines dictated a maze of gutters and downspouts. The cistern, which was

41

located under the main residence's garage slab, would require pumps and additional piping. Brown began meeting with officials from the City of Bend and the Oregon Department of Environmental Quality (DEQ) to discuss the possibility of using a constructed wetland to process both greywater and blackwater.

It took nearly a year to do it, but by November 2010, Tozer Design produced construction documents for Desert Rain I. The main residence was to include three bedrooms, a meditation room, and offices for Scott and Elliott; the design also incorporated a kitchen garden and outdoor solar oven. The graceful, rambling main house measured just less than 3,000 square feet and wrapped around a central courtyard. The house's two main shed roofs, angled south-southwest, were in dialogue with the shed roof of the detached garage, which angled the opposite way. Covered breezeways connected the main house to its garage and to a third structure, which included an accessory dwelling unit above a second garage/storage area. The structures were to feature metal roofs, soffits made from reclaimed pine, exposed timbers and reclaimed barnwood siding over stucco. Heart Springs Design's landscape design complemented the structures with stonework, native shrubs and serviceberry trees.

Just before Christmas, Timberline Construction turned in their cost estimate. Scott and Elliott were shocked. At $1.8 million, the per-square-foot cost for the Desert Rain project was just under $600; they had originally hoped to keep the cost below $350 per square foot. Throughout December, the emails flew, as team members tried to imagine ways to cut $700,000 from the cost.

"We all understood the concept and were totally on board with the project," says Hart-Henderson. "But we didn't understand what we would have to negotiate to get to the goal. There was a lot of learning and a lot of grief around that first realization… that they had spent all that money and we were not able to meet their goals."

Scott and Elliott wisely decided to put the project on hold for the holidays. Shortly after the New Year, they gathered the team at their home. The mood was somber.

"I thought, they're going to abandon the Living Building Challenge, and no problem," says Vidas. "They had a beautiful house design that was super energy efficient, with all the right materials—and they were in love with it."

After listening to each person's advice, Scott and Elliott announced their decision: they wanted to literally go back to the drawing board and start over.

42

*"When we were considering starting over, I remember saying, it's like we are hiking a mountain. We're on the trail and we have to turn back, but we don't need to go all the way to the trailhead; we just need to go back down the trail a ways, then start again."*

**ML VIDAS**

Front and Rear Elevations of the main residence, from Desert Rain I design documents by Tozer Design.

FRONT ELEVATION

SCALE 1/4" = 1'

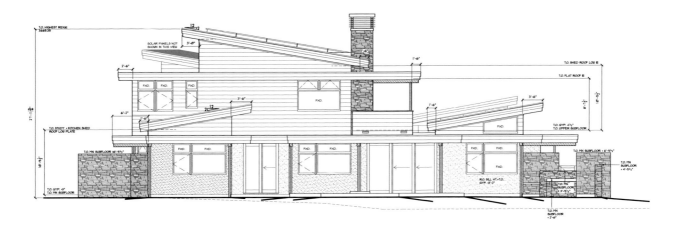

REAR ELEVATION

SCALE 1/4" = 1'

DESERT RAIN HOUSE

# INSPIRED BY PLACE

**As Tozer went to work on the design for Desert Rain II, Elliott encouraged him to "free his mind."**

"It was an opportunity to start from scratch, but to be informed by all the hard work that had come prior," he says.

A month later, when Tozer, Scott and Elliott met to unveil the new design, Tozer cleared off a table and spread out a piece of vellum, upon which he had drawn two curving lines and a dot. This simple sketch, which resembled the beginning of a painting by Spanish artist Joan Miró, was to form the central design element around which the rest of the project would radiate.

"I had this idea of just this paint brush stroke across a white canvas—an arcing stroke," says Tozer. He overlaid a second sheet of vellum on top of the first, which showed a rough sketch of the new main residence and accessory buildings. Then he explained the arcing strokes and dot.

The larger arc represented what would soon become known as the "Miró Wall": a curving wall which began outside the main residence and threaded through it. Inside, the curving wall functioned to separate the livelier, more public areas of the house from the more private, contemplative rooms. The Miró Wall emerged through the main residence on the east side, terminating in the central courtyard, where a second, smaller wall wrapped around the "dot"—the site of a large Ponderosa pine that had been sacrificed for the project.

45

# DESERT RAIN II FLOOR PLAN

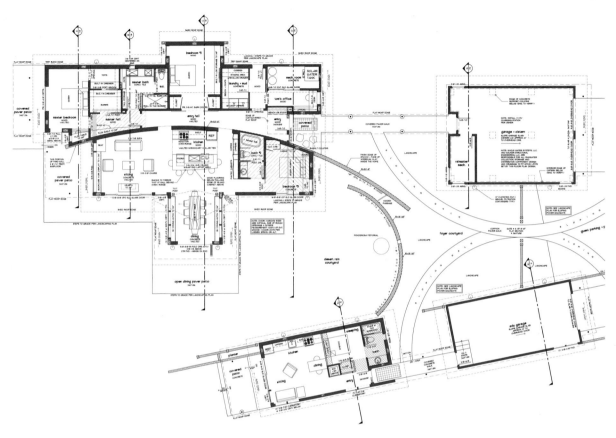

"When you're faced with the idea that something isn't working, that's pretty intense," says Tozer. "Then you think: we have a blank sheet of paper. Let's come up with something fresh and new, but incorporate all the original goals of the design and make it LBC."

Aside from this inspired design element, Desert Rain II differed from the first iteration in other major ways. The main residence had evolved from two stories to one, with more roof area but smaller square footage overall. It now featured one large shed roof with a strong solar orientation to accommodate solar panels and more efficiently capture rainwater. Smaller shed roofs—above the bedrooms and dining area—angled the opposite way. Overall, rooms were smaller and the house more compact. As for the ADU, it now consisted of a single-story structure which stood directly across the courtyard from the main residence's south façade. Detached garages for both residences

lined up with the homes' east-west axes; intersecting pathways met between the two structures. The design retained many elements of the original, including the covered breezeways and connecting pathways and integration of reclaimed materials.

The design process proceeded much more swiftly for Desert Rain II. Construction documents were submitted to the City of Bend in July 2011, and the project officially broke ground in August. As for the original design, Desert Rain I, Scott and Elliott never looked back.

"There are always ups and downs in the design and building process," says Tozer. "But to bounce back from the original design and then continue to push forward, not just financially, but emotionally, and to adopt and embrace a new design and vision is very inspiring."

# DECONSTRUCTION

Even before Scott and Elliott committed to the Living Building Challenge, they were committed to minimizing project waste. That commitment included the careful deconstruction of the two existing mill houses on the Shasta Place lots. The homes, which measured 2,000 and 1,200 square feet, were built in the early 1900s from Ponderosa pine—the primary species processed through Bend's mills. The larger structure featured stone walls and was built to accommodate a large Ponderosa pine tree, which was probably around 100 years old at the time of construction.

Typically, demolition is as simple as bringing in a bulldozer. Deconstruction is a much more hands-on process. Hazardous materials, including asbestos shingles and asbestos on the old ductwork, had to be carefully removed and disposed of. A crew from Bend's Habitat for Humanity ReStore salvaged about 3,300 pounds of materials from the two houses, including granite countertops, appliances and doors.

In September of 2009 Paul Schmitz brought in a crew from his company, Boxcar Productions, to begin the careful disassembly of the houses, piece by piece. Many other groups and individuals, some hired through a local employment agency, some from the Heart of Oregon's YouthBuild Program, helped with the deconstruction, which included removing hundreds of nails. To make the tedious task more fun, Scott whoever pulled the most nails won a small prize, usually a gift certificate to a local eatery. Much of the lumber was salvaged, taken off-site to be milled, planed and sanded, then returned to the site for later use as soffits and ceilings in the new main residence. Plywood that formed the roof decking later sheathed the walls of Desert Lookout.

The deconstruction cost significantly more than demolition and took approximately ten weeks—about five times longer than standard demolition. But the process saved many trailer-loads from the landfill, provided temporary employment and enabled the mill houses to live on through Desert Rain, which cut down on the energy cost of producing new materials. When you consider the costs to society, Elliott says, "deconstruction starts looking economically favorable."

## DECONSTRUCTION BY THE NUMBERS

**TOTAL SPENT ON DECONSTRUCTION: $54,300**

**NAIL-PULLING: $4,200**

**HAZARDOUS MATERIAL REMOVAL: $6,000**

# ART, ECOLOGY AND COMMUNITY: AL TOZER

**Al Tozer's architectural design firm, Tozer Design, has been leading the sustainability agenda in residential construction in Bend for 20-plus years.**

"Desert Rain embodies what we've been striving for since we first opened our doors," says Tozer. He jumped at the chance to use so many tools, such as passive solar design, extra-thick walls, daylighting and cross-ventilation, and to be invited to incorporate some of his own personal experiences into the design.

Tozer credits Tom Elliott and Barbara Scott for giving him free creative license, once they decided to literally go back to the drawing board and redesign Desert Rain.

"Tom knew I lived in Spain for a year, and he started thinking, maybe throw a little Barcelona in [the design]," says Tozer. That found expression through the Miró Wall, the defining element of Desert Rain II.

Tozer's background in art and biology prepared him well for a holistic approach required for the Living Building Challenge, with its ecological sensibility, including consideration of the whole life cycle of products and materials, an understanding of natural cycles and a holistic approach that considers a building's impact on the site, the neighborhood and the community.

Community has always been important to Tozer. As a high school teacher, he developed community-oriented projects to drive home lessons in global ecology. He served as a planning commissioner for the City of Bend in the 1990s, and helped rewrite the city's development code. Now he helps chair a committee that is developing a conceptual plan for revitalizing a neighborhood along Galveston Street.

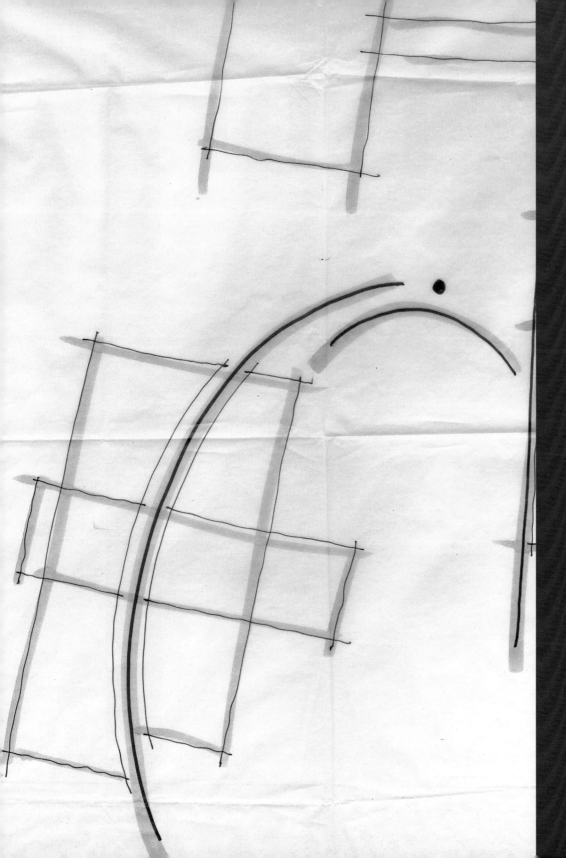

First light finding rain

Rain finding metal

Water washing wishes

Into a reservoir of hope


Sun finding pattern

Pattern housing dreams

Dreams making home

Into a reservoir of life


Art as space

Space cradles love

Love as steward

For the planet and her life


Small but not timid

Leading by example

A desert blooms

And reaches far


A team of like hearts

Pioneers in the desert

Moving the world softly

Toward a future of good


AL TOZER

49

# PART III

*Breaking Trail*

Interpreting the Petals of the
Living Building Challenge

Part III: **BREAKING TRAIL**

52

"IMAGINE A BUILDING CONSTRUCTED TO FUNCTION AS ELEGANTLY AND EFFICIENTLY AS A FLOWER; A BUILDING INFORMED BY ITS BIOREGION'S CHARACTERISTICS, AND THAT GENERATES ALL OF ITS OWN ENERGY WITH RENEWABLE RESOURCES, CAPTURES AND TREATS ALL OF ITS WATER, AND OPERATES EFFICIENTLY AND FOR MAXIMUM BEAUTY."

LIVING BUILDING CHALLENGE STANDARD 2.1

## Scott and Elliott are seeking full certification under Living Building Challenge Standard 2.1, with its seven Petals and twenty Imperatives.

Shortly after Scott and Elliott committed to the Living Building Challenge, Vidas sent the team a summary of the Imperatives and assessed the difficulty of meeting each requirement. The Ecological Flow Imperative was the only one listed with a flat "NO." The Red List Imperative was labeled merely "DIFFICULT." And indeed, the Water Petal proved the most challenging, followed by Materials; consequently, Desert Rain broke the most ground in these areas. However, none of these Petals were pursued in isolation; instead, the solutions and designs for each Petal overlapped and integrated with each other as the Desert Rain team endeavored to fulfill the Imperatives of the Living Building Challenge.

The following chapters document, Petal by Petal, many of the challenges and frustrations as well as the triumphs and innovations experienced at the "bleeding edge." Today, these Imperatives seem daunting, but in the near future they will seem as natural as a flower.

*"Everyone thought that breaking the four-minute mile was humanly impossible, bio-mechanically impossible— that physics would not allow it. It just couldn't be done until Roger Bannister did it. Then all of a sudden many others were breaking the four-minute mile."*

TOM ELLIOTT

1. SITE
2. WATER
3. ENERGY
4. HEALTH
5. MATERIALS
6. EQUITY
7. BEAUTY

53

# THE SITE PETAL

## The Genius of the Place

55

*The Site Petal:* **THE GENIUS OF THE PLACE**

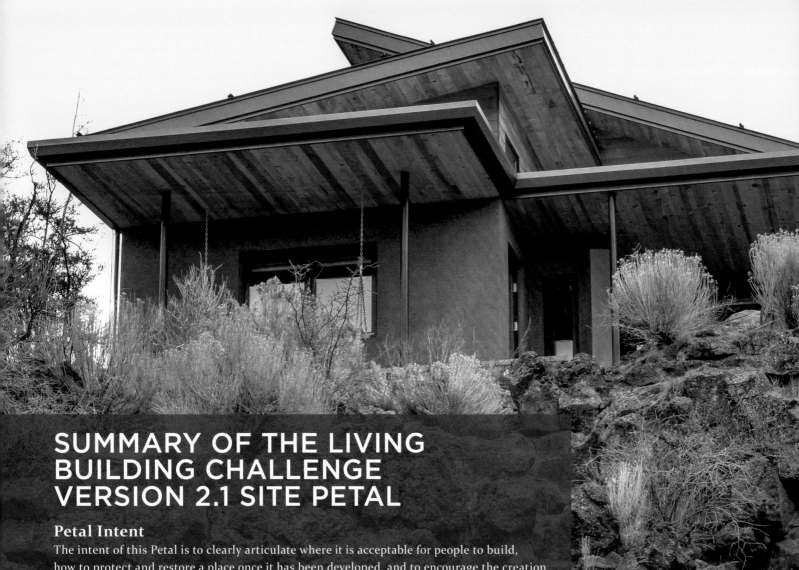

# SUMMARY OF THE LIVING BUILDING CHALLENGE VERSION 2.1 SITE PETAL

## Petal Intent

The intent of this Petal is to clearly articulate where it is acceptable for people to build, how to protect and restore a place once it has been developed, and to encourage the creation of communities that are once again based on the pedestrian rather than the automobile. Such communities should, in turn, be supported by local and regional agriculture, since no truly "sustainable" community can exist that relies on globally-sourced food production.

## Petal Imperatives
• Limits To Growth
• Urban Agriculture
• Habitat Exchange
• Car Free Living

Consult the genius of the place in all;
That tells the waters or to rise, or fall;
Or helps th' ambitious hill the heav'ns to scale,
Or scoops in circling theatres the vale;
Calls in the country, catches opening glades,
Joins willing woods, and varies shades from shades,
Now breaks, or now directs, th' intending lines;
Paints as you plant, and, as you work, designs.

ALEXANDER POPE

## IMPERATIVE:
# LIMITS TO GROWTH

**The purpose of the Site Petal is to encourage thoughtful development; to steer away from sprawling suburbs that favor cars over pedestrians and instead foster compact, connected communities that inspire self-reliance.**

This first Imperative states that projects may only be built on previously developed sites, whether greyfields or brownfields, and that projects may not be built "on or adjacent to sensitive ecological habitat." Had Scott and Elliott chosen undeveloped lots on the edge of town, they could not have pursued the Living Building Challenge. But they chose the Shasta Place lots precisely for their location in a walkable, bike-friendly neighborhood just blocks from downtown Bend. Together these lots form a pie-piece-shaped wedge, much of it on a small mesa overlooking the Deschutes River. The "crust" side drops off steeply to the west; the tip terminates at an alley to the east.

The first Imperative required the Desert Rain team to document site conditions before the project began, and stipulated that landscaping must comprise native and naturalized plants

57

DESERT RAIN HOUSE

that "emulate the density and biodiversity of the indigenous ecosystem." Al Tozer, Cecile Cuddihy and Chris Hart-Henderson met at the site several times to evaluate existing vegetation and determine the ideal locations for the new structures.

In addition to the two existing mill houses, the Shasta Place lots hosted several mature trees. Two sprawling old apple trees grew on the northern lot line. Tough junipers had established themselves on the rocky western slope. Larches, elms and a large-diameter ponderosa pine grew closer to the proposed home sites. Though Scott and Elliott preserved most of these trees—and protected and watered them throughout the construction process—Hart-Henderson and Tozer convinced them the ponderosa had to be removed, along with one larch and two elm trees. The larch and ponderosa were milled into lumber which was saved and later incorporated into the project. The excess was milled into firewood which Scott gifted to a family they connected with through Bend Habitat for Humanity.

When Hart-Henderson and Cahill evaluated the Shasta Place lots for landscaping potential, they discovered several challenges. The property's most dramatic attribute—a sheer, rocky outcropping—was also its most limiting. Much of the site was solid basalt; the little soil that was present was poor and thin. The placement of new trees was limited by a provision from the State of Oregon's plumbing code which prohibits trees within twenty feet of gutter edges if they are to be used for collecting rainwater for potable use.

The High Desert plants that thrive in the Bend area are adapted to cope with wide temperature swings and less than twelve inches of rain each year: shrubs such as rabbitbrush and sagebrush, hardy bunchgrasses and forbs such as Oregon sunshine and purple monkeyflower—and of course, the ponderosa pine.

Some native species, including Oregon grape, sagebrush and bitterweed, grew in pockets around the site, but non-native plants—annual ryegrass, cheatgrass and mustard—dominated other parts of the property. These alien species would have to be removed and disposed of in compliance with the Living Building Challenge.

Hart-Henderson and Cahill initially calculated the property's "water budget," based solely on rainwater collection and storage capacity, at an average of 83 gallons per day—hardly enough to meet the daily needs of the occupants, much less landscaping.

"At first, we assumed we were not going to irrigate at all," says Hart-Henderson. "But then Oregon started changing the rules around greywater reuse, and that opened up more opportunities." Heart Springs Design worked with Whole Water Systems on the design and placement of a constructed wetland that would process greywater; the plans also included a 5,000 gallon greywater storage tank. They calculated the greywater systems would provide an average of 60 gallons of water per day for irrigation—still a miniscule amount, especially during the critical first years when planting would need more water to establish root systems.

"I learned a lot," says Hart-Henderson. "I had to do things I'd never done before, such as calculate ET [evapo-transpiration] rates for every single plant."

Heart Springs Design's plan included a mix of native trees, shrubs, grasses and forbs, accented with permeable pathways and boulders and irrigated with an underground drip system fed by the greywater storage tank. They did not alter the site's topography, concentrating instead on building up and gently sculpting soil to direct the flow of stormwater toward existing trees, and to facilitate drainage.

The plan also included specific areas for future food gardens, a fescue meadow interspersed with native wildflowers and surprises, such as the "hidden walkway" that leads to the terraced garden below the ADU. Hart-Henderson and Cahill took care to preserve views by not planting trees directly in lines of sight.

Though implementing the landscaping plan had to wait until after construction, Heart Springs tackled the non-native annual ryegrass that dominated the western edge of the site right away. Weedkillers were out of the questions, so that left the options of smothering with mulch and/or hand-pulling. The team opted for ongoing hand-pulling, which will continue until the new plantings are established.

Just as Desert Rain was a team effort, so was the approach to the landscaping.

60

A hardy juniper grows out of the basalt on the
northwest corner of the Desert Rain site.

In summer 2013, after the greywater pond and storage
tank had been approved (and as construction of
the main residence and ADU neared completion),
Cahill revisited the landscaping plan, adding both
more diversity and increasing plant densities,
particularly in the compound's inner courtyard.

Daniel Balyeat and his crew from Daniel Balyeat
Landscaping performed the bulk of the landscape
installation, which included placing new soil,
boulders, patios and paths, along with the actual
plants. "It was a difficult installation, in part because
the process was so broken up," says Balyeat, who
frequently works with Hart-Henderson on projects.
"But we were excited because we got to do things
we'd never done before." This included building steps
out of solid basalt columns that had been cut.

Scott and Elliot brought knowledgeable friends Yvonne
Babb and Dorothy Freudenberg on board to help with
various landscaping chores. Through her business,
Your Garden Companion, Babb educates people on
how to best beautify their yards by working with the
unique soil and climate conditions of Central Oregon.
At Desert Rain, she helped install plantings and
stabilize the steep western slopes by replacing non-
native grasses with native Idaho fescue. Freudenberg,
a Master Gardener, helped with everything from
weed removal to photo-documenting the project.
Many of her images grace the pages of this book.

Also in the summer of 2013, Scott and Elliott hired Rick
Martinson of WinterCreek Restoration and Nursery.
His ecological approach helped refine the landscaping
plan for the constructed wetland and the northern
and western slopes of the property, between the main
residence and the large apple tree. Martinson not only
increased the diversity and density of plantings, he also
introduced a fungal community by inoculating plants
with micorhyzzal fungi. In addition, he tweaked the
arrangement of rocks in the hardscape to better mimic
natural conditions—what he terms "balance without
symmetry"—and to benefit plantings by directing the
flow of water and creating subtle micro-climates.

The landscaping effort included installers from Daniel Balyeat Landscaping (upper right); Rick Martinson brought in his crew from WinterCreek Restoration along with interns from OSU (below right).

61

*The Site Petal:* THE GENIUS OF THE PLACE

Rocks offer "functional beauty," says Martinson. "They create a break, and they also retain a little more water." Areas around rocks are also slightly warmer. Instead of distributing landscaping plants evenly throughout the site, he mimicked the sage steppe community by strategically clustering plants near rocks, which he calls "resource islands." These will shelter and support other smaller plants, while the spaces between islands remains unvegetated. Grouping plants this way encourages them to thrive on less irrigation water.

Martinson also used a product called Aquasmart with new plantings. This polymer-coated silica sand material absorbs and retains water so well it can reduce irrigation requirements by 50 percent.

To Hearts Springs Design's initial palette, Martinson added several new species, including cliff spirea, western yarrow and desert spray. The plants were sourced through Winter Springs Nursery, which Martinson's wife, Karen Theodore manages. Though it may seem counterintuitive at first, strategically increasing the density of plants will result in a self-sustaining landscape that does not require any supplemental irrigation water. As this landscape matures and grows, it will provide food for wildlife and become habitat for insects, birds and mammals. Martinson also designed an "insect hotel" to attract nesting pollinators, such as flies and wasps.

*"At first, we assumed we were not going to irrigate at all. But then Oregon started changing the rules around greywater reuse, and that opened up more opportunities."*

**CHRIS HART-HENDERSON**

62

DESERT RAIN HOUSE

## IMPERATIVE:
# URBAN AGRICULTURE

Every Living Building Project must provide "opportunities for urban agriculture." The percentage of the site dedicated to agriculture varies according to the project's Transect—essentially, its location, whether urban, rural or otherwise—and on its Floor Area Ratio, which is a measure of the development density.

For Desert Rain, 35 percent of the project's area was to be used for food production. This requirement posed a challenge for Heart Springs Design, since food plants—whether fruit trees or tomatoes—typically need lots of water. Balancing the requirements of both the Urban Agriculture Imperative and the Net Zero Water Imperative required a broader interpretation of "edible."

"Some plants that are technically edible—Engleman's Wood Rose, Oregon grape, serviceberry—you probably aren't going to eat," says Hart-Henderson. "On the other hand, there is plenty of food for wildlife."

They were also granted an exception for the site's steep slopes, which simply cannot host plants. Along with established apple trees already on the site, Heart Springs added serviceberry, choke cherry and elderberry trees. The list of shrubs that produce edible berries includes currants, Oregon grape and roses (for their rosehips), while wild strawberries provide an edible groundcover.

A dedicated food garden, irrigated by treated greywater, lies northeast of the main residence near the constructed wetland.

63

# HABITAT EXCHANGE

## The Habitat Imperative mandates that for each hectare of development, an equal amount of land must be set aside in perpetuity, with a minimum offset of one acre.

The Desert Rain site measures 30,371 square feet (.69722 acres), or .282 hectares. Scott and Elliott are working with the Deschutes Land Trust to meet this Imperative. The organization has protected over 8,700 acres as Community Preserves in the Central Oregon region; these include meadows, forests, canyonlands and an island in the upper Deschutes River.

Scott's daughter Lily (below) and Elliott's daughter Sarah (right) help plant ponderosa pine seedlings in Shevlin Park

64

During Desert Rain's housewarming party, Tozer, Vidas, Brown and Timberline Construction presented Scott and Elliott with two J. Livingston bicycles, which were refurbished from existing parts by Bend Velo.

## IMPERATIVE:
# CAR FREE LIVING

**All Living Building Challenge projects should "contribute towards the creation of walkable, pedestrian-oriented communities."**

The neighborhood surrounding Desert Rain includes a mix of older, Craftsman-style homes, and contemporary and remodeled dwellings of varying sizes, arranged along winding, comfortable streets. Mixed into the neighborhood are restaurants and other retail outlets. The Deschutes River and Miller's Landing, a riverfront park, are a few minutes' walk away.

"Site issues revolve around accessibility and minimizing the use of the automobile," Elliott explained to a group visiting Desert Rain from the Oregon Institute of Technology in Klamath Falls, Oregon. "We purposely picked this site because it is in a diverse neighborhood, with very easy access to everything: library, stores, and recreation."

Scott and Elliott were attracted to the Shasta Place lots because of their proximity to downtown, the hike-and-bike paths that wind along the Deschutes River, and the vibrant neighborhood community that already existed, but they were also thinking ahead to when they might not be as mobile. The central location and compound style makes Desert Rain ideal for aging in place. The garages for the residences are served by an unpaved alley lined with other homes, and the informal access, lack of fences and connecting pathways welcome visitors and residents alike.

"The other piece is that a Living Building fits into the community," says Elliott. "There's a certain sense of engagement that invites participation in the neighborhood and not just isolating ourselves."

65

# HONORING THE PONDEROSA

One of the most difficult moments of the entire project was the decision to sacrifice the large ponderosa pine that towered over one of the existing mill houses—and literally, grew out of one of its walls. The ponderosa fell within the footprint of the main residence in the initial design of Desert Rain I; attempts to "tilt" the house to avoid the tree still did not solve the problems posed by the ponderosa's presence. Its height and large canopy limited solar access. The team concluded that, even if the ponderosa was healthy at the time of construction, the impending site disturbance would likely compromise its root system and eventually kill it.

The ponderosa was cut down in the fall of 2009. Scott and Elliott held a neighborhood contest to guess its age; the winner received a spoon carved from the 201-year-old tree.

It was important to Scott and Elliott to honor the ponderosa in meaningful, enduring ways. Scott organized a team of volunteers and planted 201 ponderosa saplings in Shevlin Park, on Bend's west side. They had the ponderosa milled into lumber, which was incorporated into Desert Rain as fencing and outdoor furniture. Al Tozer highlighted the site of the ponderosa with his design for the Miró Wall, which serves as the spine for the main residence and delineates the central courtyard. Heart Springs Design planted a serviceberry tree inside the ponderosa's generous stump, and the shorter Miró Wall wraps around the young tree, creating a focal point and encouraging visitors to pause.

Finally, Bill Sturm, owner and founder of Oregon Timberworks, turned a round from the grand old pine into a memorial plaque honoring the tree. This stunning plaque now hangs on the wall just inside the east entry of the main residence.

*The Site Petal:* **THE GENIUS OF THE PLACE**

# DESERT RAIN'S LANDSCAPING PLAN INCLUDED THE FOLLOWING PLANTS:

**Meadow Species:**
Idaho Fescue
Blue Flax
Oregon Sunshine
Showy or Lowly Penstemon
Rocky Mountain Penstemon
Orange Globemallow
Desert Lupine
Silky Lupine
Pacific Lupine
Sulphur Buckwheat
Common Yarrow
Orange Sneezeweed
Indian Rice Grass
Prairie Junegrass
Linear Leaf Fleabane
Arrowleaf Balsamroot
Bee Balm
Showy Milkweed
Scarlet Gilia

**Dryland Species:**
Desert Sweet
Curlleaf Mountain Mahogany
Purple Sage
Cliff Oceanspray
Manzanita
Rabbitbrush
Wax Currant
Idaho Fescue
Bluebunch Wheatgrass
Blue Flax

**Ground Cover Species:**
Sedum Album
Sedum Acre
Pussytoes
Mixed Sempervivuvis
Wild Strawberry

**Perennials and Grasses:**
Catmint
Lavender
Yucca
Creeping Oregon Grape
Oregon Grape Holly
Woods Rose
Shrubby or Davidson's Penstemon
Palmer Penstemon
Firecracker Penstemon
Barbatus Penstemon
Spreading Phlox
Common Yarrow
Great Basin Rye
Sickle-Keeled Lupine
Indian Rice Grass
Bluebunch Wheatgrass
Globemallow

**Trees and Larger shrubs:**
Serviceberry (Amelanchier alnifolia)
Sub-Alpine Fir
Native Chokecherry
Manzanita

*In addition, Rick Martinson of WinterCreek Restoration developed plant mixes for specific areas of the site:*

**Foreground entry mix:**
Rosy Pussytoes
Silky Lupine
Sulphur Buckwheat
Bitterroot
Sandberg's Bluegrass
Linear Leaf Fleabane

**Midground entry mix:**
Prairie Rocket
Mahala Mat
Indian Blanketflower
Firecracker Penstemon

**Cliffside restoration mix:**
Sagebrush
Rabbitbrush
Globemallow
Linear Leaf Fleabane
Richardson's Penstemon
Prairie Junegrass
Mountain Snowberry
Wax Currant
Cliff Oceanspray

**Dryland shade mix:**
Woods' Strawberry
Little Flowered Penstemon
Glaucus Penstemon
Idaho Fescue
Rosy Pussytoes

**Wetland margin mix:**
Yellow Monkeyflower
Pacific Aster
Goldenrod

*The Site Petal:* **THE GENIUS OF THE PLACE**

# THE WATER PETAL

## The Limiting Factor

*The Water Petals* **THE LIMITING FACTOR**

# SUMMARY OF THE LIVING BUILDING CHALLENGE VERSION 2.1 WATER PETAL

## Petal Intent

The intent of the Water Petal is to realign how people use water and redefine "waste" in the built environment, so that water is respected as a precious resource. Scarcity of potable water is quickly becoming a serious issue as many countries around the world face severe shortages and compromised water quality. Even regions that have avoided the majority of these problems to date due to a historical presence of abundant freshwater are at risk: the impacts of climate change, highly unsustainable water use patterns, and the continued drawdown of major aquifers portent significant problems ahead.

## Petal Imperatives
• Net Zero Water
• Ecological Water Flow

*"Of all the water on Earth, only three percent is freshwater, and less than one percent is available to us in the form of rivers, lakes and aquifers that we can use to drink and grow food. To exacerbate the problem, we haven't done a very good job of taking care of that one percent. Unlike oil and gold, we can't live without freshwater. Necessity being the mother of invention, the near future will see drastic changes in how we use and value it."*

**MORGAN BROWN,**
Whole Water Systems

Most people would agree that access to fresh, clean water is a basic human right. Man-made reservoirs have allowed humans to populate and even green the deserts, and modern wastewater treatment plants clean water to ever higher standards. But centralized water systems suffer from many of the same ills as industrialized agriculture.

At an early Desert Rain team meeting, Scott poured each person a glass of water and asked if anyone could trace the water back to its source.

"No one could tell me," says Scott. "And these were people who should have known."

When water comes from a distant and seemingly endless source, it is harder for people to embrace conservation, to connect to regional watersheds and comprehend the downstream effects of the water they use and flush "away." Most municipal water treatment plants use harmful chemicals as part of the treatment process. Transporting water comes with high-energy costs, especially when it must travel uphill. In California, for example, 20 percent of the state's electricity goes to transporting, treating and heating water and wastewater. Finally, aging infrastructure

threatens water security and the environment. Much of the vast network of pipes that convey potable water and wastewater was installed just after World War II. On average, 240,000 water mains break every year, and untreated wastewater regularly breaches leaky laterals to contaminate soil and waterways. Unfortunately, upgrading this ailing infrastructure comes with a hefty price tag. By one estimate, upgrading the sewer and stormwater systems in the United States alone could cost upwards of $298 billion over the next twenty years.

The Living Building Challenge addresses all of these issues with the Water Petal. Harvesting and managing water on-site reduces the energy cost, the risk of contamination, and ensures the source from which water is drawn is replenished. The Water Petal fosters a

73

*"From a regulatory standpoint, Desert Rain broke the most ground with the Water Petal. This groundbreaking is a big part of the project's contribution to green building, in Oregon and beyond."*

**TOM ELLIOTT**

profound connection to the watershed, an understanding and appreciation of the cycles of precipitation and drought, and the motivation to use only what is needed.

The U.S. EPA supports the use of wetlands for treating wastewater and stormwater runoff; in fact, many wastewater treatment plants utilize wetlands. Although, by and large, current regulations discourage water independence, and in many cases, especially urban areas, mandate participation in centralized systems. Some Living Building Challenge projects rely on wells and on-site treatment systems that do not use chemicals, such as septic systems. However, Desert Rain's urban location prohibited most of these alternative solutions.

In early 2010 the Desert Rain team embarked on a four-year quest to meet the requirements of the Water Petal. Meeting the Petal's two Imperatives would require more persistence, collective knowledge, creative thinking and collaboration than any other of the Challenge's Petals.

"From a regulatory standpoint, Desert Rain broke the most ground with the Water Petal," says Elliott. "This groundbreaking is a big part of the project's contribution to green building, in Oregon and beyond."

# NET ZERO WATER: HARVESTING RAIN AT DESERT RAIN

**The first Imperative under the Water Petal states simply that "one hundred percent of occupants' water use must come from captured precipitation," and that water must be treated without chemicals. The City of Bend prohibits the digging of new wells, so that left one option: rainwater collection and storage.**

Whole Water Systems, led by president and founder Morgan Brown, joined the team to consult on, and design, Desert Rain's water systems. The company specializes in on-site water harvesting and wastewater treatment systems—in particular, constructed wetland bioreactors (CWBs), which use natural biological processes to clean wastewater.

The Oregon State Plumbing Code offered some guidance. In 2008, the state laid out standardized regulations for rainwater recycling in Appendix M; however, as Brown learned, this was an unfinished and untested document.

Rainwater harvest systems still fell under local jurisdiction; namely, the City of Bend Building Department. Brown recruited help from State Chief Plumbing Inspector Terry Swisher and Tim Lindsey, the regional ombudsman for the state building code, to help interpret the guidelines and to instill confidence in the proposed system. Meanwhile, Whole Water Systems Engineer David Venhuizen, Hart-Henderson and the rest of the team had been working through the many details around the system's design.

Bend's dry climate was key to sizing the storage capacity. Heart Springs Design had gathered rainfall data for Bend and came up with "ballpark" estimates for how much water could be collected from the roofs of the various structures. Venhuizen worked with twenty years' worth of rainfall data, from 1990 to 2009. Though the average annual precipitation hovered around twelve inches (including snowfall), this period also included an extreme drought year of less than seven inches and a few unusually wet years in excess of twenty inches. The trick was going to be designing a system that would carry Desert Rain through the extreme years without running out of water—or overflowing.

"It's a dynamic formula," says Vidas. "You want the cistern to be empty when you have a rain event, but you also want water to be there when you need it, during dry spells."

Other factors had to be accounted for as well. Appendix M requires that the "first flush" of a rain event be diverted from the system at a minimum rate of one gallon for every 100 square feet of roof area. Some rain would also inevitably be lost to evaporation, especially during hot summer months. Then there was the question of snowfall. In Bend, snow tends to melt off in a day or two, and is subject to the same "first flush" rules as rainfall. Although one inch of snow converts into just a fraction of water volume, the models showed that capturing snow along with rain meant the cistern could be sized smaller, and that in lean years snow could mean the difference between self-sufficiency and importing "make-up" water.

Venhuizen ran models for each of the twenty years, adjusting the values for several variables: roof area; cistern storage volume; number of occupants; and annual per capita water usage.

The models predicted the volume of overflow produced or the amount of "make-up" water that would be needed for each month. Whole Water Systems concluded a cistern with a volume of at least 30,000 gallons would carry Scott and Elliott through the worst-case dry spell without needing make-up water or resorting to extreme conservation measures. This estimate assumed a water budget of 42 gallons per day per person, well below the national average of 100 gpd.

Increasing either occupancy or daily usage would test the cistern's capacity. (In fact, one model showed that increasing occupancy by one person, make-up water would be required in seven of the twenty years, even if the cistern volume was

Keith Krewson and his crew from Central Oregon Construction Contractors form the walls for the 35,000-gallon cistern. Altogether, the cistern required 250,000 pounds of concrete.

50,000 gallons.) The team discussed designing in some "cushion" by increasing the cistern's size but Brown and Venhuizen emphasized that controlling demand would be the key to meeting the Water Petal requirements at Desert Rain.

"There is some advantage to larger storage, but we wanted to make clear that the modeling showed that usage, not cistern size, is the most critical variable," wrote Brown in an email to the rest of the team. This approach meant mindful behavior paired with efficient fixtures, no water budget for landscaping irrigation, and careful monitoring of the cistern level.

Next the team had to decide on the type of collection system and type and location of the storage tanks. Appendix M required all lines in the system to drain completely after a rain event; a so-called "dry" system would also keep standing water from freezing in the pipes. The simplest solution was a gravity-fed system in which the pipes drain into a below-grade cistern. Alternatively, tanks could be placed directly under the downspouts, or above-ground "aqueducts" could route water to an above-ground or partially submerged tank.

Scott and Elliott liked the idea of an elevated water tower powered by a traditional windmill, but the height and volume required to make such a system work ruled the idea out. Alternatively, the team looked at utilizing the existing excavated basement from the original structures for an underground cistern; however, this location would have placed the cistern too far from the points of capture.

Aesthetics and the system's specifications determined the ultimate design: a cast-in-place concrete cistern located under the centrally located main house garage. The cistern lid would also function as that building's foundation. At $1.00 per square foot, plus the additional cost of excavating twelve feet into what was mostly solid basalt, this was an expensive choice.

"In retrospect, we should have looked more closely at other options," says Vidas. "Instead of digging a deep cistern, we might have built a shallower one under a larger area." Costs for the rainwater system, including evacuation and building of the cistern, came close to $75,000.

The roofing material, gutters and downspouts, flushing and filtering system and water treatment train had to comply with both state and local building codes, and with the Living Building Challenge Imperatives under both the Water and the Materials Petals. Scott and Elliott contracted River Roofing of Bend for the roofing, gutters and downspouts. The company sourced Steelscape "Vintage" rolled steel and fabricated roof panels and other components in its shop. Appendix M accepts metal roofing for rainwater collection, but it cannot be painted, so the team had to determine whether the coated steel with a fluoropolymer finish complied. There was also some confusion over whether galvanized metal met the Living Building Challenge Red List Imperative. The older galvanizing process leached cadmium and lead—two Red List items—but the newer finishing process used to make Steelscape "Vintage" metal does not. Working out these issues required extensive communication with code officials and representatives from the ILFI, and among the members of the Desert Rain team.

Gutters and downspouts could not contain any lead solder joints, so River Roofing fabricated continuous gutters on-site, and installed screens to keep out leaves and debris. Venhuizen designed gravel filters to be installed at the base of each downspout, which would preclude the need for First Flush Diverters, saving precious water for the cistern. Brown presented the design to Oregon State Chief Plumbing Inspector Terry

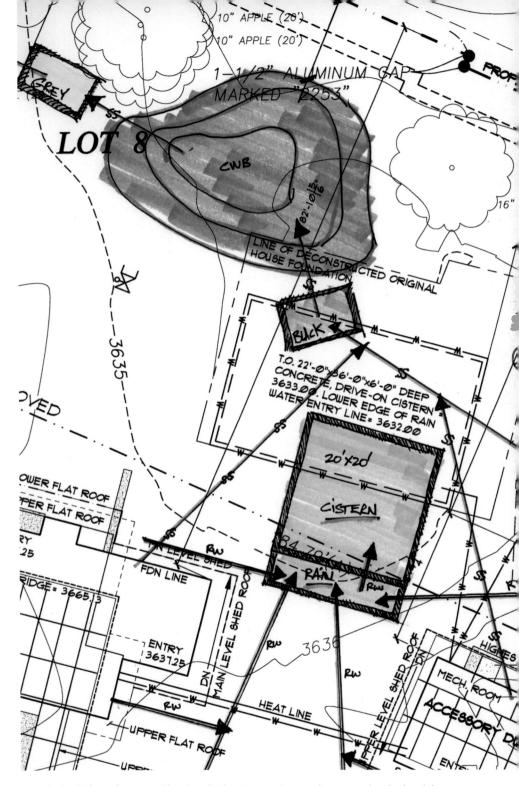

An early sketch shows the proposed locations for the rainwater cistern and constructed wetland, and the maze of plumbing lines connecting to each.

*"When you go outside and the snow
is melting and dripping through the
downspouts, and you know it's happening
in every single one... it's music to your ears.
I am grateful for every drop."*

**BARB SCOTT**

Each downspout leads to a specially-designed gravel filter, which removes most of the sediment before rainwater reaches the cistern.

Swisher. Swisher approved the design, but the Bend Building Division wanted written assurance from Oregon State officials, in addition to a Professional Engineer (P.E.) stamp of approval for not using First Flush Diverters, which would have added extra time and cost. Swisher recruited Tim Lindsey, Central Oregon Regional Coordinator for Building Codes Division, to communicate with the Bend Building Division. Swisher held a teleconference with Building Division staff to explain the solutions and followed up with a letter. Shortly afterward, Desert Rain received formal approval for its rainwater harvesting system—the first of its three water-related systems to do so.

Each gravel filter consists of a tray containing a layer of coarse rock to catch large debris, followed by eight inches of small-diameter washed gravel and a thinner, two-inch layer of half-inch washed gravel. After this initial filtering, water flows via gravity through three- and four-inch leaders to the cistern.

Desert Rain's 35,000-gallon cistern includes three chambers. Water first enters into a small chamber where any remaining sediment settles to the bottom before the water flows into the second and largest chamber. From there it flows into a third chamber, where it is routed to the pressure tanks and treatment system which are located in the pump room. The final "treatment train" consists of a sediment filter, then carbon filtration and ultraviolet (UV) disinfection. Water is pressurized, and then

directed to the three dwellings. The system is also connected to the city's potable water system, as required by the building code.

In March of 2014, Scott and Elliott switched over to the rainwater system.

"When you go outside and the snow is melting and dripping through the downspouts, and you know it's happening in every single one... it's music to your ears," says Scott. "I am grateful for every drop."

After an unusually wet spring, the cistern held 4,800 gallons. The Living Building Challenge Standard allows Scott and Elliott to fill the cistern with city water one time, before they begin their audit year, but they decided to wait and see what nature would provide. As of January 2015, the cistern held 22,400 gallons; at this rate, they may not need any city water at all.

The system was sized based on an average daily use of 42 gallons per person, but Elliott estimates they are using closer to 30. If the cistern becomes "dangerously full," a bypass valve allows them to route up to 5,000 gallons of water to the greywater system—or they can temporarily relax their conservative ways.

"We've joked about asking guests to bring their own water," says Scott. "Now we joke about getting a hot tub to use some of the excess."

IMPERATIVE:
# ECOLOGICAL WATER FLOW

**The language sounds straightforward: "One hundred percent of stormwater and used project water discharge must be managed on-site to feed the project's internal water demands or released onto adjacent sites for management through acceptable natural time-scale surface flow, groundwater recharge, agricultural use or adjacent property needs." Yet this Imperative almost prevented the Desert Rain team from pursuing full certification.**

In March 2010, Elliott, Tozer and Vidas met with representatives from the City of Bend's Public Works Department to discuss options; specifically, to discover whether the City of Bend would allow a well or rainwater collection for potable use, the use of a constructed wetland for processing waste on-site, and/or a greywater system to reduce demand.

"When discussing waste treatment, we received a very polite 'No,'" wrote Vidas in a summary of that meeting. "They repeated that DEQ does not allow on-site waste treatment if the building is within 300 feet of existing city sewer service. They would not support any efforts to circumvent this requirement." The City also emphasized that Bend's waste treatment facility operates to very high standards, even providing wetland and bird habitat.

In an early report, Morgan Brown outlined three options: Use greywater for flushing toilets, using a state-approved product; design a constructed wetland bioreactor (CWB) that would process all wastewater, including "blackwater" from toilets, or design separate wetlands to process greywater and blackwater, respectively.

Brown proposed the third option in anticipation of Oregon's fledgling greywater code, not yet formalized. In 2009, the state had approved the establishment of such a code, and had charged the Department of Environmental Quality (DEQ) with developing the permitting process. However, no one expected the new greywater code to come into effect until the Fall of 2011 at the earliest, and no one could predict exactly what types of water reuse would be allowed.

The team decided on Option Two, with a caveat: They would seek approval of the CWB as a "pretreatment system" for all wastewater. Although the treated effluent would still flow

*"The process bore a strong similarity to the early days of grid-tied solar—now broadly accepted. Many utilities fought it tooth and nail for years, until enough pockets of successful implementation made light of their concerns. "Grid-tied sewer" is in a similar situation to the early days of solar. While conventional wisdom on solar has shifted to the broad benefits of decentralized systems, the benefits of on-site wastewater treatment are only widely accepted among the sustainable crowd. The Desert Rain project has the potential of creating a significant crack in that dike and could contribute meaningfully to its eventual demise."*

**MORGAN BROWN**

into Bend's sewer system, the strategy would anticipate a future when the regulations would allow on-site treatment, at which point Desert Rain could disconnect from the city's system. In the meantime, the on-site pretreatment would ease the burden on Bend's wastewater treatment system and align with the spirit of the Ecological Flow Imperative. And, as Brown pointed out, installing the system would at least educate others by demonstrating an on-site treatment solution. Hopefully, other projects could use its existence as leverage to change the code that requires sewer connection.

Brown received preliminary verbal and email approval from the City of Bend Public Works Department for the pretreatment system as early as spring of 2010. Whole Water Systems had proceeded with the design in good faith, but a year and a half later, there was a glitch. The Building Division Manager suddenly entered the discussion, and told the team there was "no way" the wetland would be approved as a pretreatment system. He insisted the City of Bend Building Division had jurisdiction over the CWB. Brown argued that anything two feet outside the building envelope falls under the umbrella of Public Works, but the Building Division would not budge.

Brown decided to seek a more formal statement from the City of Bend Public Works stating their authority over pretreatment systems. Because Oregon DEQ shared this domain, he also decided to involve local DEQ officials. He knew he had to navigate carefully through this uncharted territory.

"You only get one chance to make a first impression," Brown cautioned the rest of the team in an email. "It can be hard to come back again and again with incrementally more information. It pays to do it carefully."

In early 2012, three different DEQ officials provided written statements verifying the City of Bend Public Works had jurisdiction over Desert Rain's proposed pretreatment system. Brown presented these statements, along with detailed document describing the proposed system, which included EPA support for the technology, to the Building Division Manager.

"We discussed how new approaches—no matter how sustainable or worthy—create conflicts with established procedures, and that to succeed we needed key people helping to find a way to 'yes,'" says Brown. "We knew he could find code that he could interpret as banning our system."

A long phone conversation left Brown with little hope that the Building Division Manager was willing to be one of those "key people." But just as it seemed they were running out of options, another avenue opened.

In Spring of 2012, DEQ released guidelines for three levels, or tiers, of permitted greywater systems. The simplest, or Tier I system, allows the use of raw or filtered greywater for subsurface irrigation, but prohibits storage. TierII requires greywater to be treated either chemically or biologically. The treated greywater may be used in both subsurface and surface drip irrigation; it may also be stored.

Brown proposed a new approach: Repackage the CWB as part of a Tier II greywater treatment system. The wetland could then be sized so that it might someday receive both greywater and blackwater, once regulations allow it. They had a viable plan.

"It's not like people haven't tried building off-grid before. What makes Tom and Barb's situation unique is they're building in an urban area where services are fully available and service suppliers expect you to hook up to them. There aren't very many of those free-thinking, off-grid folks who have the money and the commitment to work through the bureaucracy. That is what makes Desert Rain so unique."

**CHRIS HART-HENDERSON**

Before filling with gravel, the constructed wetland was lined with Bentomat, a woven, geosynthetic fabric the encapsulates a layer of sodium bentonite.

81

*The Water Petal:* THE LIMITING FACTOR

# GETTING TO YES

**The Desert Rain team submitted an application for a 2042 Tier II permit to the Oregon DEQ in December of 2012. As was required, the application included design documents, an Operation and Maintenance (O&M) Manual, and a completed DEQ Greywater Flow Worksheet. Diane Naglee, the Natural Resource Specialist for DEQ who handled the application, worked with Brown and Hart-Henderson on clarifications and revisions. These included removing a utility sink from the system, reconfiguring irrigation zones to ensure no greywater would flow off the property, and adding more details to the O&M Manual.**

Meanwhile, the Bend Building Division was making demands; specifically, department officials wanted a professional engineer (P.E.) to inspect the greywater system and all of the outdoor plumbing to ensure it had been installed correctly.

"A significant objective of the Desert Rain project is to make it easier to pursue sustainable construction," wrote Brown in a letter to the City of Bend. "We are very concerned that this P.E. requirement would make it very unlikely that other homes would install greywater systems in Bend." Then the winds of fortune shifted. Robert Anderson, the plumbing plans examiner, returned

to work from a health absence. Once again Terry Swisher stepped in, convincing Anderson that the DEQ, not the Bend Building Division, was responsible for the outdoor plumbing review. In March of 2013 the Building Division agreed to allow a third-party inspector from their approved list to review the greywater system, and to verify it was installed according to Whole Water System's plans. This was a much less onerous—and less expensive— alternative to the P.E. stamp they had insisted on earlier.

"The odyssey through the permitting process has been intellectually and professionally frustrating and fascinating," says Brown. "The code book is full of reasons to say no. To get to yes, the risks must be removed."

In June 2013, Desert Rain became the first residence in the state of Oregon to receive a residential wastewater permit, which effectively granted permission to use a constructed wetland bioreactor to treat greywater from sinks, showers and laundry, and to store the treated greywater for use in landscape irrigation.

Biologist John Grove and Engineer Patrick Fitzgerald designed the wetland to treat all wastewater for a family of four; consequently, it is larger than it currently needs to be. Covering 450 square feet at the waterline and measuring less than four feet deep, the wetland contains a shallow gravel bed topped with finer material, and is landscaped with water-loving sedges and grasses. An earthen berm and impermeable barrier keep water from running off into the surrounding landscape. The water level sits several centimeters below the top of the gravel, ensuring the wetland does not become a breeding pond for mosquitoes and preventing accidental contact with pathogens.

Greywater first flows via gravity into a primary treatment tank, where solids settle out. From there it flows into the wetland itself, where it is retained for an average of seven days.

Natural biological processes and a host of aerobic and anaerobic bacteria cleanse the wastewater. Microbes that live on the gravel process nutrients in the water, as do the roots of the water-loving plants that landscape the CWB. The variety of microhabitats and the interactions between roots and microbes ensure that the water is completely treated to EPA tertiary standards—levels suitable for subsurface and drip irrigation.

DEQ rules prohibit using treated greywater on landscaping when soils are saturated or when the ground is frozen. Normally, greywater would be redirected to the city

sewer service during such times, but of course, this was not allowable. Consequently, Desert Rain's system had to include adequate capacity for storing greywater on-site.

Whole Water Systems and Heart Springs Design collaborated to size the storage tanks. They considered several factors: the amount of greywater produced per day; the wetland' volume and the capacity of the landscaping to "use" the greywater.

In the DEQ permit application, Hart-Henderson had to "prove" that no irrigation water would discharge into state waters—in other words, that all of the water would be taken up by plants and/or evaporate. In this case, Bend's dry climate helped the cause, especially for the critical winter periods.

"Even in worst-case months, when application is restricted because of frozen or saturated soils, the landscaping will still be able to use at least 500 gallons a month," explains Hart-Henderson.

The treated water flows to a 1,000 gallon holding tank located below the wetland; from there it is pumped to a 5,000 gallon reclaimed water tank, located underground, near the main residence's garage and adjacent to the rainwater cistern. This tank feeds the landscape irrigation system and one water feature on the grounds. The irrigation system includes five zones and provides water to 5,200 square feet of landscaped area.

Altogether, the system includes 6,500 gallons of storage. A water feature helps dispose of excess treated greywater during the winter months when the water is not needed to irrigate landscaping. By law, the system also connects to the city sewer. But all of the system's built-in redundancy is designed to ensure that all treated greywater stays on-site, and out of the sewers.

# THE FINAL BARRIER

**Desert Rain was designed under the assumption that "conventional" toilets would route waste to the wetland, via gravity. Now, the team members faced limited options, which included retrofitting composting toilets into the design or giving up on the Ecological Flow Imperative in hopes that they could eventually use the CWB to process all wastewater.**

In April of 2012, Elliott first proposed using "dehydrating toilets," which would essentially desiccate human waste before sending it to a central composting chamber. And so the concept of Desert Throne was born.

As with all of Desert Rain's water-related systems, the team faced a host of issues and obstacles. The City of Bend Building Division would approve composting toilets, but they had to be NSF-certified (third-party certifier of plumbing products and materials); the City also required plumbing be roughed in for at least one standard toilet in both the main residence and the ADU. Any gravity-fed central composting chamber would need to be installed below grade. Scott and Elliott preferred the Phoenix system, manufactured by Advanced Composting Systems. Not only did the Montana-based company enjoy a good reputation, the composting chamber was large enough to handle waste from all of Desert Rain's flush toilets. On the down side, the larger chamber measured seven feet tall, which meant more expensive excavating.

There was also an issue of what to do with the effluent from the dishwasher. Oregon's new greywater code prohibited this waste from feeding into the greywater system, as the high nutrient content could potentially overtax it. This hindrance meant either routing the effluent to the sewer or to whatever blackwater system the team designed. But the extra volume would introduce a larger volume of liquid to the composting chamber, potentially slowing the process and creating anaerobic—that is, stinky—conditions. Evaporating off some of the water before it reached the composting chamber could solve the problem, but would require energy to heat air inside the evaporating chamber. An evaporator would also introduce a new element that city officials had no experience with, inevitably slowing the approval process.

By Fall of 2012, the team had navigated these multiple issues and Whole Water Systems designed a schematic of Desert Throne. Scott and Elliott had abandoned plans for Desert Breeze, the third dwelling unit, in favor of a complex they were calling Desert Station. The basement of the existing garage would house the Phoenix composting chamber and evaporating unit. A new building adjacent to the existing garage would include a composting toilet and also serve as a storage shed and root cellar.

The composting chamber would receive wastewater from all toilets, and whatever effluent from the dishwasher that had not been evaporated off. After rough filtering, effluent from the dishwasher would then flow into a storage tank "evaporator,"

Desert Lookout, the project's final structure, includes the composting chamber below a dwelling unit on the second floor.

85

# COMPOSTING HEADQUARTERS

The Phoenix Composting Toilet and chamber receives waste from vacuum-flush toilets in the main residence and ADU and from the composting toilet located upstairs. The chamber is "charged" with wood shavings, peat moss, and water to create an environment conducive to biological decomposition. A shaft with tines within the unit rotates to mix the decomposing waste and introduce oxygen. Worms will eventually be introduced to speed the process along.

Four SolarSheat panels mounted on the exterior walls of Desert Lookout heat air that circulates through the "Evapotron." Designed by Advanced Composting Systems, the same company the provided the Phoenix unit, the Evapotron evaporates water from the dishwasher and leachate from the composting unit itself.

By pioneering the use of vacuum toilets in combination with a composting chamber, Desert Rain is demonstrating a viable onsite blackwater treatment solution for urban settings.

which would also receive any leachate (excess liquid) from the composting chamber. Solar air panels would heat the air and route it to the evaporator, removing as much of the water as possible.

Although this proposed system was not strictly illegal (no codes existed to interpret it), there were other issues. Even though Scott and Elliott planned to use ultra-efficient toilets that only required one gallon per flush, the Phoenix composter could only handle an average of five gallons of liquid per day—and that included dishwasher waste. They also could not justify the expense for building what was essentially a glorified outhouse.

In March 2013, Scott and Elliott found themselves in an all-too-familiar situation.

"In light of the increasing complexity of the design for the blackwater system, we decided to drop the existing proposal and move into a redesign from ground up," says Elliott. Just as the decision to abandon the original design for Desert Rain paved the way for Desert Rain II, this bold decision opened up opportunities.

Scott and Elliott decided to deconstruct the old garage, remove the existing foundation and slab and pursue a new design, which combined elements of Desert Breeze and Desert Station. The two-story carriage house would include an apartment on the second floor served by a bathroom with a composting toilet; the ground floor would house the Phoenix composting system, garage and storage. The design change allowed Timberline and Tozer to separate the plans for the new structure from the permit for Desert Rain, which included the main house, ADU, associated garages, constructed wetland and other infrastructure.

"This allowed the approval for the greywater and plumbing systems to proceed and reduced the likelihood of DEQ or Bend's Building Division to cause further delay in final Desert Rain approval," explains Brown.

Meanwhile, the team would seek approval for the pioneering blackwater system as an Alternative Engineered Design, as defined by the Oregon State Plumbing Code. The Building Division officials hinted they would consider this radical system, but since it was beyond the scope of NSF certification for composting toilets, they required an Oregon Professional Engineer (P.E.) stamp for both the proposed vacuum plumbing system, dishwasher discharge plumbing and the evaporator. Understandably, the Building Division also wanted assurance that the system would not create strong odors.

Brown chose to work with Portland-based Interface Engineering. Not only did the firm have experience with green building, including the Living Building Challenge, Principal Jon Gray served as chair of the state plumbing board. Though Interface typically worked on larger commercial projects, they were eager to participate in designing systems for a cutting-edge Living Building Challenge project.

Tozer went to work designing a new building, which Scott and Elliott christened Desert Lookout. Meanwhile, Elliott had been researching vacuum toilets, similar to those used in airplanes and cruise ships. Not only did they use very little water (one quart per flush), they would not require "fall" by gravity, which meant the composting chamber would not have to be located below grade.

Advanced Composting Systems (ACS) had used Sealand Dometic vacuum toilets with its systems, but expressed concern about the distance between the dwellings and Desert Lookout. Consequently, ACS recommended installing a small holding tank and lift station in between these two sites. Interface expressed concern that a lift station would not work with such small amounts of wastewater. After researching several other companies, the team finally settled on Jets, a Norwegian company that manufactures vacuum toilets for ships. The Jets toilets were affordable and well-made, and the system would work without the lift station, but there was one potential glitch. Although Jets' water-saving systems have also been widely used in buildings throughout Europe, Australia and Brazil, they had never been

installed in a residence in the United States. The team proceeded with the hope that the Building Division would accept the system if it was included in the liability under Interface's P.E. stamp.

Tozer submitted plans for Desert Lookout in late 2013; by February 2014 the team had satisfied all requests from the Plans Examiner. Just when approval seemed imminent, the team hit another wall. Health issues had forced Robert Anderson, the planning examiner for the City of Bend, to take a leave of absence. His replacement, who was not familiar with the project, told Scott and Elliott that the City of Bend would not be able to grant a permit for Desert Lookout with the proposed blackwater system.

Frustrated and disappointed, Elliott wrote an email to the Building Division, requesting a meeting with Brown, Tozer and John McMichael, the engineer from Pace Engineering. That same day, Elliott received an unexpected surprise in his Inbox:

"Mr. Elliot, I am back to work temporarily and am going to sign off on the plumbing alternate method portion of your permit. Sorry for the confusion while I was out. No need for a meeting."

Serendipitously, Robert Anderson had returned to work for a few days. With the stroke of a pen, he cut through the last obstacle. In April of 2014, the City of Bend finally granted approval for Desert Lookout—including the composting system and evaporator that would serve the entire compound.

# THE ENERGY PETAL

## Centered Around the Sun

89

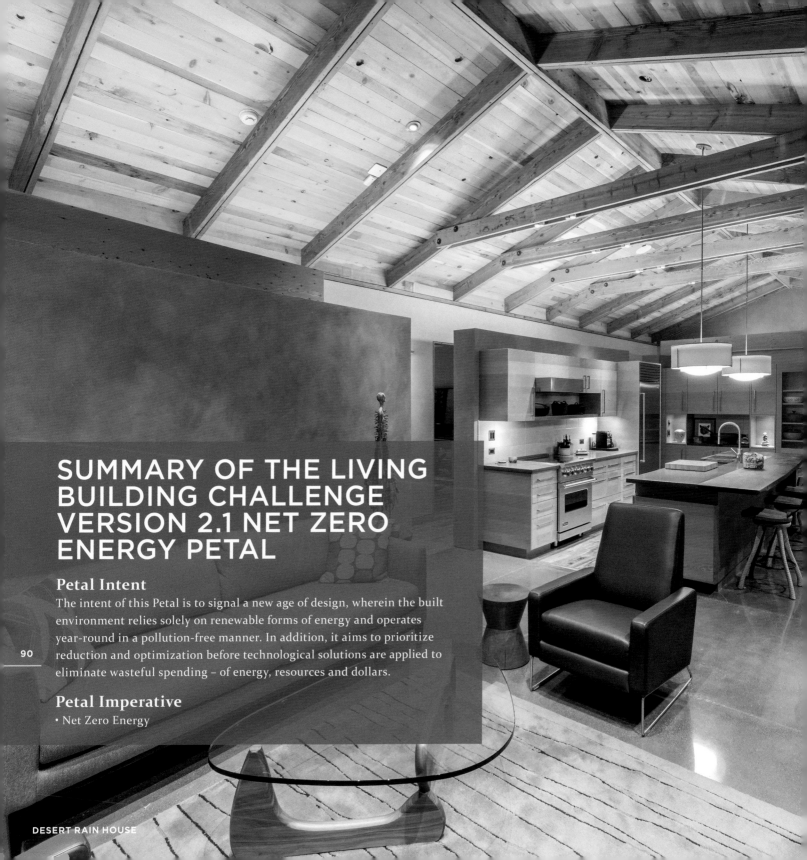

# SUMMARY OF THE LIVING BUILDING CHALLENGE VERSION 2.1 NET ZERO ENERGY PETAL

## Petal Intent

The intent of this Petal is to signal a new age of design, wherein the built environment relies solely on renewable forms of energy and operates year-round in a pollution-free manner. In addition, it aims to prioritize reduction and optimization before technological solutions are applied to eliminate wasteful spending – of energy, resources and dollars.

## Petal Imperative
• Net Zero Energy

# THE ENERGY PETAL

**The intent of this Petal, with its one Imperative, is simple: all Living Building Challenge Projects must produce at least as much energy as they consume. The term is "net zero energy," and it is a concept that is rapidly entering the mainstream consciousness, as more and more people recognize the critical importance of reducing emissions through thoughtful design strategies and particular attention to the sources that heat, cool and power our buildings.**

Many leading scientists and more than a few political leaders acknowledge that climate change, exacerbated by the burning of fossil fuels, may well be the biggest challenge that humanity has ever faced. We have already passed a critical threshold of 350 parts of atmospheric $CO_2$ per million—the maximum concentration to avoid global warming, sea level rise and a host of related changes—lending urgency to the shared obligation of all countries to minimize current and future emissions.

In the United States, buildings account for 39 percent of carbon emissions. In recognition of the built environment's contribution, the U.S. Department of Energy has been setting step-wise goals to lead the industry toward a net zero energy building standard; some states, California in particular, are fast-tracking this process. The U.S. Green Building Council recognizes green buildings as "a vital tool in the fight against climate change," and reports that the average LEED certified building uses 32 percent less electricity and saves 350 metric tons of $CO_2$ emissions annually. The Living Building Challenge takes the stance that society cannot afford to wait: the technology to create net zero buildings is available now; we just need the collective will to mandate net zero. In fact, the net zero goal is just a step toward an even more ambitious vision: net-positive buildings and communities which, taking a cue from nature, contribute more than they consume. (Living Building Challenge 3.0 requires buildings to produce 105 percent of their energy, and to provide storage for resiliency.)

The Challenge's net zero energy Imperative aligned with Scott and Elliot's commitment to sustainability in all aspects of their lives, including transportation. With that in mind, they wanted Desert Rain to function as a "power house," producing enough energy not only to supply all three dwellings and the site's infrastructure, but also to charge two electric vehicles.

91

The main residence includes large amounts of glazing on both the west and south façades, but deep overhangs help prevent the harsh summer sun from overheating the home.

*"We wanted to design a house that acts like a shade tree in summer."*

AL TOZER

# AN EFFICIENT SHELL

**The Living Building Challenge does not lay a path for achieving the net zero energy goal, although there are some underlying assumptions: focus first on reducing energy demand through all available design strategies, then make up the difference with on-site renewable energy sources, typically wind generation and solar power.**

"Our first approach was to have as efficient an envelope as possible," says Elliott.

Tozer Design worked with Timberline to create this envelope. Staggered, double-wall construction was used for all three dwellings. Exterior 2 x 4 walls were framed twenty-four inches on center, with the second interior wall offset by twelve inches. This framing method allows for greater (and flexible) depths, creating deeper cavities for insulation and reducing thermal bridging—the external-internal heat transfer that occurs between wood framing members.

Each building features a different framing and insulation package. Wall thicknesses in the main residence vary from twelve inches on the colder north, west and east façades (excepting the mechanical room) to ten inches on the south façade. Similarly, the south-facing walls in the ADU and Desert Lookout are not as thick as the rest of the exterior walls.

The roof framing consists of specialized trusses, built by Quality Truss from FSC-certified lumber sourced through Parr Lumber Company of Oregon. A false ceiling was created by matching the slope of the main shed roof at the ridge, and the resulting attic is a "warm" or conditioned space, as the insulation lies against the roof sheathing.

The floor of the main residence consists of a concrete stem wall and grade beam structure supporting floor joists, subfloor and a concrete slab. The slab supports a hydronic heating system and varies in thickness depending on whether it serves as finished floor or underlies wood flooring. (The ADU and Desert Lookout were also built with crawlspace foundations.)

Tozer Design worked with Timberline Construction to reduce thermal bridging wherever possible. For instance, rigid foam insulation completely isolates the foundation from the rest of the framing. The plan also minimized the amount of solid wood around windows and other openings.

The design of Desert Rain optimizes passive solar orientation, especially for the main residence. Both it and the ADU are oriented on east-west axes; both buildings are longer than they are wide, and include significantly more glazing on the south façades, compared to the north. Deep overhangs block direct sun in summer but allow for solar gain in the winter months, when the sun follows a lower path across the sky.

"We wanted to design a house that acts like a shade tree in summer," says Tozer. The design also takes advantage of materials which help regulate indoor temperatures by storing and slowly releasing heat. A double layer of drywall throughout the main residence combines with the finish plaster to create thermal mass; the concrete slab floor also performs this type of function.

# INSULATION AND AIR-SEALING

**Because of its high R-value per inch, Timberline and Tozer Design selected closed-cell spray foam as the insulation of choice for Desert Rain House. Insulation installer Energy Conservation Insulation (ECI) applied the material in phases: a base coat air-sealed the walls; a second application covered plumbing and electrical lines, once in place. The phased installation ensured the material would off-gas completely before being covered.**

Other types of insulation were used in the project. In the main residence, UltraTouch cotton batts, made from 80 percent recycled blue jeans, fill interior walls and ceilings and provide sound-proofing. Desert Lookout features a "hybrid" insulation system: two to three inches of closed-cell spray foam, followed by blown-in fiberglass to fill the cavities. Knauf EcoBatt insulation, comprised of sand and at least 62 percent post-consumer recycled material, insulates the garages.

Resulting R-values (see chart below) in the main residence are well above code.

Air sealing is critical for regulating indoor air temperatures. Timberline Construction performed whole-house caulking that included all joints between sheets of exterior sheathing and between framing members. After installing insulation, ECI used thermal imaging—performed from both the inside of the house and the outside, at night—to identify any leaks or weak spots in the envelope.

"We discovered that the steel gang-nail plates in the roof trusses transfer quite a bit of heat," says Fagan. "We came back and re-foamed several places."

Blower door tests also helped the team evaluate the building's air-tightness integrity. A test performed after insulation was installed, but before drywall, measured leakage in the main residence at 0.70 air changes per hour (ach)—very close to the Passive House standard of 0.60 ach.

| | OREGON RESIDENTIAL CODE | DESERT RAIN (INCLUDES MAIN RESIDENCE AND DESERT SOL) |
|---|---|---|
| Walls | R-21 | R-50 |
| Roof | R-38 | R-72 |
| Floors | R-30 | R-50 |

# GOOD GLAZING

**Even though the revamped design reduced some windows sizes, the ratio of glazing in the main residence is still quite high. The choice of windows and doors was critical for minimizing heat loss (and unwanted heat gain) through these "holes in the envelope." Ultimately, Scott and Elliott went with Canadian manufacturer Loewen Windows.**

Not only does Loewen make all of the components of their windows at their Manitoba factory, it sources most of its wood from FSC-certified forests and recycles all scrap, including sawdust, which helps power the manufacturing plant. The company also promotes the longevity of its products by designing components to be easily removed and repaired. Even Loewen's packaging is completely recyclable.

"The windows don't come in tidy, shrink-wrapped bundles, but nothing goes to the landfill," says Elliott.

For Scott especially, generous amounts of glazing provide that much-needed visual connection between the indoors and the outdoors. The windows also bring in ample light, so that during the day, artificial lighting is seldom needed.

The metal-clad wood windows are triple glazed and filled with argon gas; thermal spacer bars ensure two full half-inch air spaces between panes, which provide more insulating value.

95

*The Energy Petal:* **CENTERED AROUND THE SUN**

Radiant heat tubing snakes through the concrete slab in the main residence. Advanced framing techniques, extra-thick walls, spray foam insulation, and careful air sealing contribute to a tight envelope.

# A MULTI-PRONGED ENERGY STRATEGY

**Bruce Sullivan and Matt Douglas, Green Building Consultants for Earth Advantage, performed the energy modeling for Desert Rain House, which helped guide decisions leading to lower energy demand and consumption throughout the project. "The biggest thing they did to reduce demand was reducing the size of the main house," says Douglas. Working with a set of plans, he plugged in numbers for variables such as insulation type, wall thickness, and the energy loads from select appliances and lighting fixtures.**

Heating and cooling eat up a good portion of a typical home's energy budget—48 percent, according to the Department of Energy. Water heating accounts for another 15 percent. The tight envelopes of the buildings significantly reduced energy demand; the next step was determining how to most efficiently heat living spaces and domestic hot water. Scott and Elliott chose an infloor radiant heat system, which allowed them to combine water and space heating. The system is powered primarily by a solar thermal drainback system, installed by the Bend-based company Bobcat and Sun.

"In most high-efficiency, high-end custom homes, solar thermal heating supplements the main heating system," says Elliott. "In this case, our solar thermal system is supplemented by a heat pump."

The sun heats a propylene glycol solution in thermal collectors on the roof. The glycol protects the system from freezing during Bend's cold winter conditions. The liquid solution effectively transfers heat to water in a tank via a heat exchanger, then "drains back" into a smaller tank when no more heating is needed, which, in turn, protects the storage tank from overheating. Bobcat and Sun also installed the radiant heating (hydronic system) which relies on hot water flowing through tubing buried in the concrete slab. Because the heat emanates from the floor and slowly rises, occupants typically feel comfortable at lower air temperatures as compared to a space heated with a forced-air furnace.

A Daikin Altherma Monobloc air-to-water electric heat pump works in tandem with the solar thermal system. This unit extracts heat from the outside air by passing it over a heat exchanger. A second heat exchanger "rejects" the heat into water, and the cooled refrigerant returns to repeat the cycle again. This type of heat pump is extremely efficient, extracting three to five kilowatt-hours of usable heat for every kilowatt-hour of energy consumed. It also includes an electric back-up heater for extreme cold weather. The ADU and Desert Lookout rely exclusively on these highly efficient heat pumps.

97

The mechanical room houses the energy recovery ventilator and the network of plumbing lines for the solar thermal system.

98

Reducing energy for space and water heating was paramount, but several other strategies helped reduce overall demand. All appliances are rated Energy Star or better. Lighting fixtures utilize LED lamps, which use 20 to 25 percent of the energy of incandescent bulbs and last up to twenty-five times longer. "Kill" switches on the entertainment centers allow Scott and Elliott to turn all components off at once, so they do not draw phantom loads while not in use. A Nest Learning Thermostat helps them optimize the radiant floor system.

But, as important as all of Desert Rain's energy efficiency features are, one variable will determine if Desert Rain lives up to its potential—occupant behavior.

"There are all kinds of examples of efficient buildings that do not perform because of human behavior," says Elliott. He and Scott are good about "self-policing": turning off lights, conserving water, and so on. On the other hand, they admit to leaving windows open in the dead of winter because they like a cold bedroom, or keeping the shades open on a starry night. Beyond the "learning thermostat," they did not invest in systems that would control their home's functions for them. "We intentionally veered away from too much automation," says Elliott.

Daily engagement with their home's functions fosters awareness—reminding Scott and Elliott of their important roles in saving energy and water.

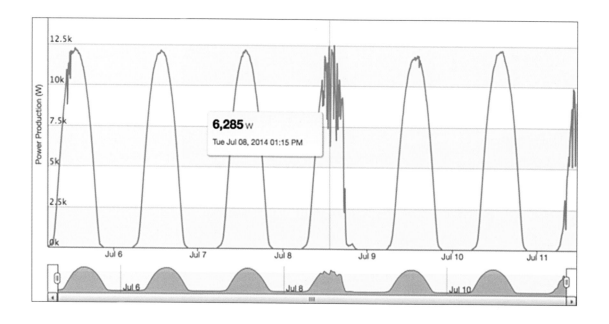

This chart shows the energy production of Desert Rain's solar array in July of 2014. The spikes and dips track the sun's daily path.

# HARVESTING THE SUN'S POWER

**To fulfill its function as a demonstration project, Scott and Elliott wanted Desert Rain to feature as many renewable energy systems as possible. The buildings use the sun to heat water and generate electricity and heat air from the "Evapotron" composting system. Early on, Scott and Elliott also looked into harnessing the wind to supplement solar power in meeting Desert Rain's energy demand; however, they were surprised to learn that two vertical turbines required significant wind speeds to generate useful amounts of energy.**

They installed an anemometer at the site to gather wind speed data, and determined winds were not strong or consistent enough to justify using turbines. Another factor influenced their decision. They approached all of their neighbors about the possibility of installing turbines, and although nearly all supported the idea, one neighbor balked. Ultimately, good relations with neighbors weighed in and won out.

The decision not to utilize wind power meant Desert Rain would rely exclusively on solar energy as its renewable energy source. E2 Solar, a Bend-based company, performed the site analysis and the installation of Desert Rain's solar PV system, working with Matt Douglas' energy model to size the array. By converting demand, as measured in BTUs, to kilowatt-

hours, Mike Hewitt of E2 Solar originally sized Desert Rain's PV array at 8.5kW. But Scott and Elliott wanted to have enough energy to charge two electric vehicles, estimating 15,000 miles annually for each car. That changing electrical demand meant nearly doubling the capacity of the system.

The 14.95 kW array consists of sixty-five 255 Sunmodule monocrystalline panels from the Oregon manufacturer SolarWorld. Forty-four of the panels cover the main residence's south-facing shed roof; the remaining twenty-one are mounted on the detached garage's roof. Enphase micro-inverters allow each module to function independently and to be individually monitored.

99

# TRIAL AND ERROR: WORKING WITH HOT AIR

Four SolarSheat 1500g panels power the "Evapotron," an essential part of the blackwater composting system housed in the ground floor of Desert Lookout. The Evapotron removes water from the waste effluent coming from toilets and dishwashers.

The system's panels work simply: a fan draws air into the bottom of the panels; once heated, the air blows through ducts on the other side. For aesthetic reasons, Scott and Elliott decided to have three panels mounted on the south-facing exterior wall of Desert Lookout. Unfortunately, the eave overhang would partially shade them in summer, hindering their performance. The representative from Advanced Composting Systems was concerned the three panels would not provide enough heat to evaporate the liquids at the required rate.

"There was a lot of head-scratching over the hot air panels," admits Elliott. The team decided to lower the panels and add a fourth one on the west façade. In addition, Timberline trimmed the eave, which had already been finished with siding.

Meanwhile, the HVAC installer had used a slightly smaller pipe to transport the hot air coming out of the panels, which means a smaller but hotter volume of air will reach the Evapotron. Ultimately, the fourth panel may not have been necessary. If that turns out to be the case, the excess hot air will used to heat the composting room itself.

Central Oregon is an excellent place to harness solar energy, with many sunny summer days and cold, clear winter days. At Desert Rain, there were no issues with shading, but the site orientation, which angles just slightly west, lowered its solar resource score to just below a perfect 1.41.

E2 estimated that Desert Rain's array would generate 19,842 killowatt-hours per year, just offsetting annual energy demand—including electric vehicle charging. However, the array was sized before Desert Lookout was built; additional loads, such as pumps for the greywater wetland and composting system, also had not been accounted for. Because there were so many variables, Scott and Elliott had Desert Lookout pre-wired to accommodate additional solar panels, if needed in the future.

"We've tried to build resilience into the system without adding a lot of cost," says Elliott.

Through the Enphase energy management system, Elliott and Scott are able to monitor their PV system, observing energy production and their consumption cycle in predictable trends. In December and January, consumption peaks and production dips; conversely, production is highest in July and August, when demand is lowest. After a year, Desert Rain's PV array is performing better than expected— and demand is lower than predicted.

"The models are based on averages," says Hewitt. "They do not account for variations in human behavior."

In July of 2014, Desert Rain produced five times as much energy as was consumed—and that included energy needed to power the construction of the Desert Lookout building. That month of energy data gave Scott and Elliott a glimpse of a net positive future—a future where buildings emulate nature, and contribute more than they consume.

**DESERT RAIN HOUSE**

# DESERT RAIN'S BUILDERS:
## JAMES FAGAN AND KRISTIAN WILLMAN

Kristian Willman and James Fagan know building. Through their company, Timberline Construction, they have carved out a niche in Central Oregon's custom home market, "moving toward green" with projects that incorporate sustainable materials, energy efficiency, and extensive jobsite recycling.

After Desert Rain, Willman and Fagan can claim they know Living Buildings, too. Willman started out as project manager. Bringing his high energy and enthusiasm to the project, he worked closely with Tozer Design to implement Scott and Elliott's ambitious green agenda.

"Tom and Barb knew we'd pushed the envelope on some alternative techniques, including straw bale, insulating concrete forms (ICF) and structural insulated panel (SIP) construction," says Willman. "But this was different. They wanted to go all the way."

After Scott and Elliott decided to scrap the design for Desert Rain I, Fagan took over as project manager. An Oregon native, he began his building career in the San Francisco Bay Area, digging ditches on construction sites. He learned the trade from the man who would become his father-in-law, a hands-on designer-builder who insisted on being onsite for every job.

"He almost treated it like a school," says Fagan. "We did everything from excavation to finish carpentry. I'm glad I learned that way, because I understand every aspect of building."

Fagan had the right temperament to roll with the many changes, delays and unconventional scheduling that came with the (uncharted) territory of building one of the first residential projects to fully qualify for the Living Building Challenge.

"I introduced the term 'slow build' early on," says Fagan. "If everyone could afford to take their time, it would be brilliant."

In Bend, it is typical for general contractors to sub out many aspects of the job, even framing. Timberline brought along their many experienced subcontractors to the Desert Rain project, but only after ensuring they were on board with the Living Building Challenge agenda.

"People in the construction industry can be stubborn. If they've been doing something the same way for years, they want to keep doing it that way," say Fagan. "I've been the opposite, always wanting to move forward."

*The Energy Petal:* **CENTERED AROUND THE SUN**

# LIGHTING DESERT RAIN

Light-emitting diodes, or LEDs, use half the energy of compact fluorescent bulbs, and a fraction of the energy of incandescent lighting. Further, the bulbs have a much longer lifespan and contain no mercury, which is toxic to humans and the environment. Scott and Elliott knew they wanted to use mostly LEDs throughout Desert Rain, but at the time the availability and quality of LED fixtures and lamps was limited. They observed that light output was low, the lamps tended to create hotspots rather than diffuse even light, and the color tended toward the cool end of the visible spectrum.

"We purchased many types of LEDs, both locally and on-line," says Scott. "We tried one bulb after another. Then we tried a local light designer. Their plan consisted of about 100 canned lights in straight lines."

Initially, Al Tozer and Wendy Knight took on the task of the lighting plan; however, they had little experience designing with LEDs. They were concerned with not only choosing energy-efficient fixtures that provided warm, comfortable lighting, but finding efficient, low-voltage lighting controls. Given the many requirements, they decided to hire an experienced designer who specialized in sustainable lighting design. They found such a person in Zach Suchara, a LEED-certified architect and principal with the Portland-based firm Luma Lighting. Suchara was also working on the lighting design for another Living Building Challenge project—the Bullitt Center in Seattle—which enabled Desert Rain to take good advantage of products that had already been vetted.

Suchara was able to source unique fixtures, such as the "flower" lights in the bathroom. His design balances daylight with artificial light, and incorporates reflective and up-lighting. "For example, the Miró Wall doesn't just have simple gimbal lighting," says Knight. "Instead, light floods the wall consistently, all the way from the inside to the outside."

Scott and Elliott believe lighting should be considered early on in the design process in order to achieve an elegant, energy-efficient balance between natural and artificial illumination.

"The lighting in our home is a delight," says Elliott. "It's a huge dimension of its beauty, comfort and health."

102

"Traditional lighting can be over-exaggerated and even blinding. I disliked the glare from these type of lights and didn't realize there were other choices. When I sit in my home with a book or a cup of tea in the evening, I am surrounded by the warmth of the glow and reflections off the reclaimed wood. I don't experience an awareness of light fixtures; it's more like being in the glow (and warmth) of a campfire."

**BARB SCOTT**

103

# THE
# HEALTH
# PETAL

## Creating Restorative Spaces

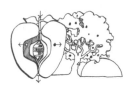

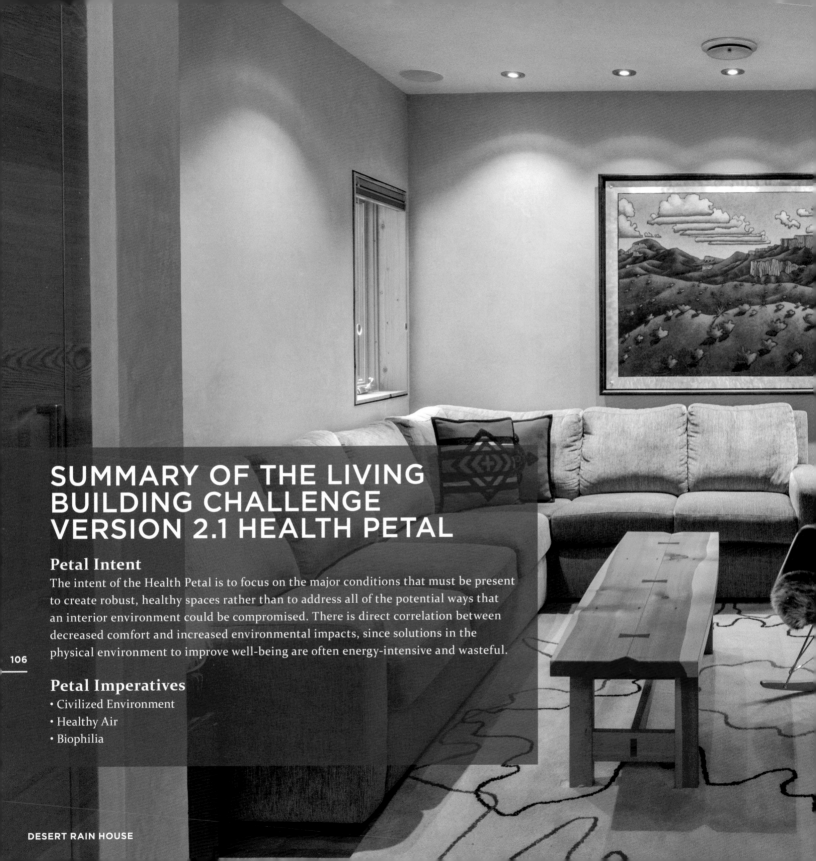

# SUMMARY OF THE LIVING BUILDING CHALLENGE VERSION 2.1 HEALTH PETAL

## Petal Intent

The intent of the Health Petal is to focus on the major conditions that must be present to create robust, healthy spaces rather than to address all of the potential ways that an interior environment could be compromised. There is direct correlation between decreased comfort and increased environmental impacts, since solutions in the physical environment to improve well-being are often energy-intensive and wasteful.

## Petal Imperatives

• Civilized Environment
• Healthy Air
• Biophilia

**What is a healthy building? Certainly it is one that is free of toxic materials and products, and one that guarantees a continuous supply of fresh air. But a building that truly promotes health should also emulate and connect with nature, rather than cutting people off from the outside environment.**

Nature is good for us, physically, mentally and spiritually; this central idea is encapsulated in the word "biophilia"—the natural affinity humans feel for other living things. As with the Beauty Petal, the inclusion of Biophilia as a prerequisite for creating a Living Building speaks to a broader definition of sustainability, one that includes physical and spiritual health.

# IMPERATIVE:
# CIVILIZED ENVIRONMENT

**The Civilized Environment Imperative stipulates that all Living Buildings shall include an adequate ratio of operable windows to ensure access to fresh air and daylight. At Desert Rain House the indoor-outdoor connection was paramount.**

Although the team chose superior triple-paned windows, a high ratio of glazing still can compromise energy performance. However, the carefully measured trade-off was worth it to Scott and Elliott, who were both accustomed to living in country settings.

"It's very important to us to feel like we are inside and outside at the same time," says Scott. Consequently, all three residences feature ample windows, including glass doors that lead to discrete outdoor destinations, such as patios, gardens and the solar oven.

# IMPERATIVE:
# HEALTHY AIR

**Rather than stating what elements will compromise indoor air quality, the Healthy Air Imperative sets minimum standards for achieving it:**

- All projects must include a dirt track-in system, both inside and outside. This feature is to prevent dust and debris from accumulating inside.

- Equipment must be installed to monitor indoor levels of carbon monoxide, temperature and humidity.

- Certain rooms, including kitchens and bathrooms, must be adequately ventilated.

In addition, air quality testing must be conducted before occupancy and (at least) nine months afterward. This test measures both respirable suspended particulate matter (RSPM) and total volatile organic compounds (VOCs). Although maximum levels are named, the project is not disqualified outright if it exceeds these levels.

Beyond meeting these requirements, the use of natural materials and Red List-compliant sealants and finishes—or no finishes at all—makes for non-toxic indoor environments.

The American Clay plaster product used on the interior walls and ceilings of Desert Rain is completely free of VOCs and resists mold growth. The myrtlewood floors are finished with Osmo, a Swedish product made from plant-based oils and waxes. The wood ceilings and diamond-polished concrete floors are not finished with anything at all.

An energy recovery ventilator captures waste heat, but also ensures a steady influx of fresh air into the main residence. To reduce the impact of electro-magnetic frequencies (EMFs), electrician Mike Wagnon wired the bedrooms with metal clad (MC) cable.

Scott and Elliott's behavior also influences indoor air quality. They open windows daily and a ceiling fan in the bedroom also helps to circulate air. The only "cleaning products" in the pantry are vinegar and Everclear, a grain alcohol used to clean counters, toilets, windows, metal fixtures and more.

*"It's very important to us to feel like we are inside and outside at the same time."*

BARB SCOTT

IMPERATIVE:
# BIOPHILIA

**For the Biophilia Imperative, the Living Building Challenge draws on the work of Dr. Stephen R. Kellert, an expert social ecologist who pioneered the incorporation of biophilia into design with his groundbreaking work, *Biophilic Design: The Theory, Science and Practice of Bringing Buildings to Life*. The Biophilia Imperative stipulates that each of six biophilic elements, as defined by Kellert, must be incorporated into the project every 2,000 m².**

Walking through the Desert Rain site is a biophilic treasure hunt that engages all senses in a positive way. On every scale, both inside and outside the buildings, connections to the High Desert region and the animals and plants that thrive there can be found.

## ENVIRONMENTAL FEATURES

These features include characteristics of the natural environment, such as sunlight, fresh air and plants as well as natural colors and materials. The extensive use of natural materials and "organic" colors characterizes all of the buildings at Desert Rain, from the warm gray exterior plaster to the salmon tones of the larger Miró Wall—colors inspired by the native Manzanita, and complemented by stone and wood. Outside, reclaimed greywater bubbles over rocks, replicating the sound and freshness of a small brook. Inside, the combination of reclaimed wood and clay plasters creates warm, clean-smelling spaces filled with natural light.

Cabinetmaker Gabriel Dansky carefully matched the grain on the cabinet faces to create landscapes-like images.

## NATURAL SHAPES AND FORMS

This aspect of biophilia can be interpreted widely, to include any shape that mimics a form found in nature, and applies at the macro and micro levels; for example, the curving Miró Wall that threads through the main residence—and the smaller, echoing wall—mimic the winding Deschutes River. A full scale example is the building itself, with its large overhangs, acting "like a shade tree" in summer.

On a smaller scale, cabinetmaker Gabriel Dansky carefully matched the grain on kitchen cabinets to create patterns that evoke natural landscapes. The arrangement of light fixtures in the stairwell at Desert Lookout follows the Golden Ratio, a common proportion found in everything from nautilus shells to finger joints. Other features, both inside and outside, use "sacred geometry" to create harmonious, nature-inspired places.

## NATURAL PATTERNS AND PROCESSES

This category includes designs that stimulate several senses, simulate the qualities of organic growth, facilitate the organization of complexity, or reflect the process of aging and the passage of time.

American Clay plaster was chosen for all interior wall finishes, not only for its earthy hues, but also for its breathability. Rather than cutting a building off from changing weather conditions outside, it moderates humidity by absorbing and releasing moisture. In the process, the clay also releases negative ions—believed to capture free radicals and stimulate the production of mood-elevating serotonin.

"People touch the American Clay walls," says Scott. "They love how it looks; it draws them in."

111

The pendant lights illuminating the stairs in Desert Lookout are carefully placed to approximate the proportions of the golden spiral, found in nature in nautilus shells and spiral galaxies.

112

At certain times of the year, sun coming in from the south-facing windows in the main residence works with the curving Miró Wall to cast a shadow-line on the floor, which changes over time—not unlike the patterns of light and shadow found in canyons or desert landscapes.

## LIGHT AND SPACE

Natural lighting and a feeling of spaciousness help people feel that they are in a natural setting, as do more subtle features, such as the integration of light, space, and mass.

In all three residences, well located windows allow for constant views of the surrounding landscape, including resident wildlife, near-distant trees and the mountains beyond. "It's not just about having a view; it's about perspective," says Elliott. The open plans and vaulted ceilings create a feeling of spaciousness, and the curving wall in the main residence offers a more organic experience of interior space, compared to conventional rectangular rooms and linear hallways.

## PLACE-BASED RELATIONSHIPS

Landscaping features, the use of local and indigenous materials, and ties to historic and cultural traditions can create connections between buildings and the distinctive geographical, ecological, and cultural characteristics of particular places.

The use of native plants in the landscaping throughout the property forges a direct connection with the region, and Rick Martinson's ecology-based landscaping takes it a step further. Emulating the native sage-steppe community serves a practical purpose—conserving water and creating optimal conditions for the native plants to thrive on-site—and it also grounds Desert Rain more specifically in the indigenous landscape.

The use of salvaged materials links Desert Rain to unique historical stories. Although the structures are contemporary in design, the use of wood, particularly reclaimed and sustainably harvested wood, connects them to Pacific Northwest building traditions, and points to a future where these traditions are reinterpreted so that they sustain both the region's forests and its communities. The use of clay—one of the oldest building materials—creates a link to a still more ancient past.

In the main residence, the sightlines through doorways are used to frame paintings that are hung on the clay-finished walls behind them. This thoughtful placement of art, much of it created by local and regional artists, also taps into the history and cultural heritage of the West.

"People gravitate to these pieces, like I've never seen in any of my other houses," says Scott.

## EVOLVED HUMAN RELATIONSHIPS TO NATURE

Features that reflect the natural tendency to affiliate with nature evoke a feeling of being in a coherent and legible environment, create a sense of prospect and refuge, or simulate living growth and development. Visitors subtly experience the layers of intention that have been built into Desert Rain as soon as they enter the site. The main passage leads them from a relatively stark landscape along a curved pathway through richly diverse native vegetation. The first thing encountered upon entering the main residence is the Ponderosa memorial slab.

"The Ponderosa memorial is a tangible reminder of our connection to that tree and, through its vivid structure of growth rings, to the continuity of nature," says Elliott.

Once inside, one experiences the feeling of being enveloped by the combined natural warmth of so many organic elements; at the same time the spaciousness and views create a feeling of expansiveness. Put another way, Desert Rain feels good. It stimulates the senses while calming the spirit, much as a forest or starkly beautiful desert landscape does, cultivating the sense of "prospect and refuge" Kellert describes.

"This home feels like a sanctuary to me, more than any other place I've ever lived" says Scott.

113

# THE MATERIALS PETAL

Considering the Whole Life Cycle

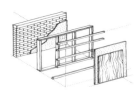

*The Materials Petal:* **CONSIDERING THE WHOLE LIFE CYCLE**

# SUMMARY OF THE LIVING BUILDING CHALLENGE VERSION 2.1 MATERIALS PETAL

## Petal Intent

The intent of this Petal is to introduce a successful materials economy that is non-toxic, transparent and socially equitable. The Imperatives in this section aim to remove the worst known offending materials and practices.

## Petal Imperatives

- Red List
- Appropriate Sourcing
- Responsible Industry
- Embodied Carbon Footprint
- Conservation + Reuse

*"We really worked as a team on the Materials Petal. Al would have design ideas and Jim would bring in his construction perspective. I'd weigh in on the LBC compliance side. We worked closely, figuring things out. I don't believe a Living Building Challenge project can be successful without this fundamental level of trust and respect."*

**MARY LOUISE (ML) VIDAS**

The intent of the Materials Petal is to "induce a materials economy that is non-toxic, transparent and socially equitable." This is a formidable task, given that our current materials economy, enabled by inexpensive fossil fuel, is largely driven by bottom-line profits that externalize the true cost to the environment, laborers and communities all along the economic value chain. Successful competition in the traditional materials economy hinges on the assumption that the lowest price will always be the most attractive attribute to consumers.

Fortunately, people are more than consumers, and concern for the triple bottom line of People, Profits and Planet is driving many manufacturers to embrace sustainable manufacturing processes, reduce waste and, in turn, demand responsible practices all along the chain of custody.

The Materials Petal, with its five Imperatives, takes a comprehensive approach to building, considering the impacts all along the way:

from the chemical composition of materials to the distance products have to travel; from the impact of resource extraction to a product's longevity and recyclability; from the project's carbon footprint to the generation of waste on the jobsite. For the Desert Rain team, the Materials Petal ranked alongside the Water Petal as the most challenging of all, yet it also spawned some of the project's most rewarding and fruitful outcomes.

117

# MAKING A ROAD:
# THE CHALLENGE OF VETTING MATERIALS

The creation of industry-specific certifications, such as the Forest Stewardship Council certification for sustainably-harvested wood products, is making it easier to source materials that have been extracted and manufactured responsibly, with the people and planet in mind. Still, there is much uncharted territory. Teams working on the first wave of Living Building Challenge projects have expressed frustration at the lack of information and transparency for evaluating building products.

Sustainability Consultant and Living Building Challenge Ambassador Mary Louise (ML) Vidas took on the task of vetting every single material for Desert Rain. This responsibility meant ensuring that each product and material met the criteria for the Challenge's Red List and Appropriate Sourcing Imperatives and for some, the Responsible Industry Imperative. With over 500 materials in play on the Desert Rain project, such an enormous task required a highly organized approach. Early on, Vidas developed a spreadsheet protocol, based on the basic form provided by the ILFI but customized to include the team's tracking notes, vetting details and approval process.

Point people were assigned to funnel information about prospective products to Vidas in the form of "e-data sheets." Vidas developed an electronic template, which included all of the pertinent information categories as they related to the Materials Petal. Kevin Lorda of Timberline Construction kept ongoing lists for materials and products gathered from the many subcontractors and he emailed Vidas prioritized groups of e-data sheets to ensure the vetting process would not cause unwanted delays. Wendy Knight of Tozer Design did the same for interior finishes, products and materials, "pre-vetting" them as best she could, so as not to waste Vidas' time. Chris Hart-

Henderson was responsible for landscaping materials, from gravel to irrigation valves to the actual plants used throughout the site.

"Usually we just design, but they put it back on us to research and vet materials that met the Red List requirements," says Hart-Henderson. "It required patience and dedication."

Vidas' strategy was to find the Material Safety Data Sheet (MSDS) for each product, and identify a technical specialist from the company who could answer key questions. Still, there were challenges. The MSDS is only required to list "hazardous" materials. The team discovered that often products contain "proprietary materials," which some companies are reluctant to disclose.

If there was still uncertainty about whether a material met all of the Red List criteria, Vidas submitted a question via the Living Building Challenge's Dialogue, the forum available to ILFI Community members. Some situations unearthed previously unexplored technical complexities; consequently, ILFI staff sometimes had trouble keeping up with all of the requests, and often weeks would pass before questions were answered. "You want support, because you feel you're so out

on the edge, but it (information) is not there," says Vidas. "Not because people aren't willing; it's just not there."

When the Desert Rain project began, the Living Building Challenge was relatively new and few projects were certified. Fortunately, over the years resources have improved and the Dialogue itself has changed. Based in part on feedback from early Living Building Challenge projects like the Omega Center, Phipps Conservatory and Bertschi School, the ILFI has developed individual Petal Handbooks to clarify the Challenge Imperatives and to provide a unified reference for project teams. Product spreadsheets from specific projects have also been made available, although they do not address the issue of proximity.

"With all the detail in the Standard and in the Dialogue, and now in the Handbooks, there appears to be so many resources to support an LBC project," says Vidas. "But the reality is that it (the Challenge) is a moving target. So many situations are very specific to any given project. Every time you turn around you are blazing a new trail."

The Declare initiative, introduced in Fall of 2012, provides an avenue for manufacturers to directly register products and prove that they are meeting Living Building Challenge criteria. Vidas believes the Declare database will streamline the evaluation process for future teams working on Living Building Challenge projects, and help ease the pressure off the people responsible for vetting materials.

# IMPERATIVE:
# RED LIST

**The Red List Imperative stipulates that a Living Building Challenge project cannot contain any of fourteen items included in the Red List, a compilation of "worst-in-class" chemicals and substances.**

Numerous Red List items are found in commonly used building materials. For example, the glues used to bind layers of plywood together contain formaldehyde, and polyvinyl chloride (PVC) has largely replaced copper as a less expensive option for plumbing lines, fittings, window frames and other applications. Manufacturers of spray foam insulation add halogenated flame retardants to products in order to meet building code requirements for fire safety. Because substitutes are not currently available for some of these items, the Living Building Challenge has granted temporary exceptions. However, before special exemptions are granted, someone from the project team must write a letter to the manufacturers, urging them to develop products that are free of Red List ingredients.

The Desert Rain team took advantage of the temporary "small components" and Red List exceptions for several materials; for example, some of the wiring includes a PVC coating, as Timberline Construction could not find a PVC-free substitute that met the state building code. Similarly, the closed-cell spray foam insulation utilized at Desert Rain, chosen for its high R-values and air-sealing capabilities, contains flame retardant chemicals from the Red List.

The Red List requirement also sparked several innovative solutions—some of which will never be seen. For example, the Red List precludes the use of lumber impregnated with arsenic, creosote, or pentachlorophenol. This so-called pressure-treated lumber is often used to frame areas that could potentially encounter moisture, such as underneath floors. Though some manufacturers are pressure-treating lumber with less toxic chemicals, Timberline Construction worked with Parr Lumber to come up with an alternative that did not use chemical treatments at all. They considered Western juniper, which is naturally rot and pest resistant. This tree species has been encroaching upon large areas of the sage-steppe habitat in Eastern Oregon, where it monopolizes water resources and outcompetes other plants. Although juniper could be sourced locally, it was not FSC certified, so the team decided not to risk using it. Ultimately, Timberline chose Western red cedar for the sill plates. Sourced through Sustainable Northwest Woods, the 100 percent FSC-certified cedar was harvested as part of a restorative forestry management program at Homestead Girl Scout Camp in Zigzag, Oregon.

Instead of PVC, all plumbing lines in Desert Rain are made from cross-linked polyethylene, commonly referred to as PEX. This strong, flexible piping and tubing also runs through the radiant floor system in the main residence. Outside, Hart-Henderson sourced PVC-free tubing for the landscaping irrigation.

## THE PROJECT CANNOT CONTAIN ANY OF THE FOLLOWING RED LIST MATERIALS OR CHEMICALS:

- Alkylphenols
- Asbestos
- Cadmium
- Chlorinated Polyethylene and Chlorosulfonated Polyethlene
- Chlorobenzenes
- Chlorofluorocarbons (CFCs) and Hydrochlorofluorocarbons (HCFCs)
- Chloroprene (Neoprene)
- Chromium
- Chlorinated Polyvinyl Chloride (CPVC)
- Formaldehyde (added)
- Halogenated Flame Retardants (HFRs)
- Lead (added)
- Mercury
- Polychlorinated Biphenyls (PCBs)
- Perfluorinated Compounds (PFCs)
- Phthalates
- Polyvinyl Chloride (PVC)
- Polyvinylidene Chloride (PVDC)
- Short Chain Chlorinated Paraffins
- Wood treatments containing Creosote, Arsenic or Pentachlorophenol
- Volatile Organic Compounds (VOCs)

121

Heavy materials, such as these landscape boulders, pavers and concrete, must come from within a 500 km radius of the project site.

DESERT RAIN HOUSE

IMPERATIVE:
# APPROPRIATE SOURCING

**This Imperative seeks to minimize the transportation energy cost of materials and promote local economies by charging that materials and products must be sourced as close to the project site as possible.**

"There is a large carbon footprint associated with the transportation of materials and that is always externalized," says Elliott. "Society pays for it, rather than the person actually using the material. We need to pay current dollars for those things, or else minimize them."

Essentially, heavy materials, such as stone and concrete, must be sourced within a smaller radius than "light" materials. Those materials that enhance the energy performance of a building, such as solar panels, can come from farther away. A chart lays out the specific criteria by grouping categories of materials into different zones.

Heart Springs Design was responsible for many of Desert Rain's heaviest materials: pavers, gravel, soil and plant material. The project's landscaping reflects the regional environment, beyond just the native and climate-adapted plantings. The Holland permeable pavers, sourced from Willamette Graystone, were made at the company's manufacturing facility near Eugene, Oregon. Concrete for some of the patios was salvaged

from the foundations of the original structures. Bend-based Empire Stone provided gravel, drain rock and one of the most striking landscape elements: the columnar basalt that forms the exterior stair treads. The six-sided columns were squared off and heat-treated to achieve a bullnose on each tread.

Sourced from Moses Lake, Washington, the basalt quarry lies just within the allowable 500-km radius. Because it was such a close call, Manager Brian Salazar offered to verify the distance from Bend to the quarry with his truck's odometer. His attitude typified many of the subcontractors' and suppliers' response to the Living Building Challenge requirements, says Hart-Henderson.

"He was always asking, how are we going to solve this?"

Vidas concurs, "We were all exchanging emails and discussing this issue. Then Kevin [Lorda] realized we could measure as the crow flies, and we were in!"

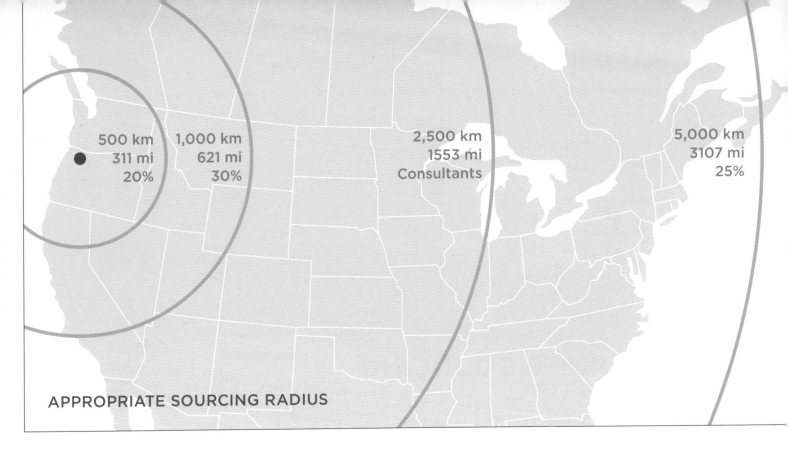

500 km
311 mi
20%

1,000 km
621 mi
30%

2,500 km
1553 mi
Consultants

5,000 km
3107 mi
25%

APPROPRIATE SOURCING RADIUS

The team also took advantage of some allowed exceptions to this Imperative. For example, although Knight sourced lighting fixtures that were made in the United States, she and Vidas could not find domestically-manufactured LED lamps; nearly all LED lamps are made in China, and none are made in North America.

Heart Springs Design applied for a small components exception from the Appropriate Sourcing Imperative for some of the irrigation valves and fittings. Although they were sourced from a supplier in Fresno, California, the items were manufactured in Israel, well beyond the 5,000 km radius allowed for irrigation equipment.

At times the Appropriate Sourcing Imperative created unexpected challenges. Timberline Construction and the framing crew agreed to substitute American-made nails for the Chinese variety they usually used. The American nails, sourced from Illinois-based Maze Nails, were made from heavy-gauge steel and were slightly longer; consequently, they did not always drive completely into the wood when fired from a framing gun, and they had to be finished by hand the rest of the way.

## IMPERATIVE:
# RESPONSIBLE INDUSTRY

The Responsible Industry Imperative stipulates that projects "must advocate for the creation and adoption of third-party standards for sustainable resource extraction and fair labor practices." The Imperative currently applies to raw materials, including timber, stone, rock and metal, although the Living Future Institute anticipates making other industries comply with this Imperative in the near future.

Requirements for lumber are more specific. All wood used in a project must be sourced from forests certified by the Forest Stewardship Council (FSC), from salvaged sources or have been cleared from the project site.

Reclaimed woods was used extensively, both inside and outside.

# GOOD WOOD

**Irresponsible logging not only devastates habitat, it devastates human communities. FSC certification ensures that fair labor practices and sustainable logging practices are employed all along the supply chain. The Forest Stewardship Council follows rules for responsible forest management known as the ten FSC Principles that include provisions for workers' rights and the protection of indigenous peoples' rights.**

Desert Rain House celebrates the beauty of the region's most abundant resources: its forests. All of the structures are wood framed, from the floor joists and wall studs to the truss members and sheathing. Wood accents building exteriors with cedar siding and tongue-and-groove cedar in the eave soffits, and adds beauty to the landscaping in the form of fences and gates. Inside, wood complements the clay plaster walls in flooring, cabinetry, ceilings and countertops.

Timber is a major industry in the Pacific Northwest, so finding lumber that met both the Responsible Industry and Appropriate Sourcing Criteria was not difficult,

although both certified and reclaimed lumber are more expensive than so-called "conventional" lumber.

Timberline Construction worked with Parr Lumber and Sustainable Northwest Wood to obtain FSC-certified lumber for Desert Rain. A subsidiary of non-profit Sustainable Northwest, Sustainable Northwest Wood sources all of its lumber from forests in the Pacific Northwest managed to the standards of the Forest Stewardship Council. The company also deliberately patronizes smaller mills in rural communities, in order to bolster their economies.

125

Sustainable Northwest Wood searched long and hard for a supplier of locally harvested, FSC-certified plywood. The company stocks AC and CDX grades in several thicknesses, made from wood sourced from FSC-certified forests in Northern California and milled in Oregon's Umpqua Valley. The plywood is NAUF, or no added urea formaldehyde, so it also complies with the Red List Imperative.

The structures at Desert Rain celebrate some of Oregon's most iconic and abundant tree species: ponderosa pine, Douglas-fir, Western red cedar and Oregon myrtle. One of the elements that gives the project its warm look is the extensive integration of salvaged wood, both inside and out. While much of this lumber came from the deconstructed mill houses on-site, some of it was salvaged from a barn in Prineville, about an hour northeast of Bend.

This old barn originally served as a storage shed for potatoes, but in recent years had attracted secondary school students looking for a place to hang out unsupervised. Concerned about liability should one of them get hurt, the family decided to have it torn down. Douglas-fir, alder and ponderosa pine lumber was salvaged from the structure to be used for rafters and collar ties in Desert Rain's main residence; some was also used in the tongue and groove soffits and interior ceilings. Larger timbers were repurposed as posts between the dining room and kitchen.

Oregon myrtle, prized for its rich grain patterns and highly variable coloring, grows in a narrow band of coastal forest from Central Oregon to the San Francisco Bay Area, where it is called California bay laurel. Myrtlewood sourced from Slice Recovery Sawmill in Coquille, Oregon was used for flooring in the hallway and bedrooms of the main residence, and throughout the ADU.

126

# IMPERATIVE:
# EMBODIED ENERGY

This Imperative directs project teams to track the project's carbon footprint in two ways: from the original construction and by projecting the "carbon cost" of replacement parts and materials in the future. To account for this impact the Imperative provides for a one-time offset tied to the project boundary. ML Vidas is working with Elliott to calculate Desert Rain's carbon footprint, using one of the Living Building Challenge's recommended carbon calculators.

In addition, and in keeping with the spirit of mindfulness and respect for resources, the Desert Rain team tried to minimize the carbon footprint of the project through the careful selection of long-lasting materials with lower embodied energy.

Desert Rain House includes a significant amount of concrete throughout the project. Concrete forms the foundations for all the structures and lines the walls of the 35,000-gallon cistern and 5,000-gallon greywater cistern. The larger cistern alone required 250,000 pounds of concrete: 160,000 pounds for the walls and 90,000 pounds for the nine-inch "lid," which also serves as the foundation for the main residence's garage.

As a building material, concrete has no equal: it is strong, versatile, durable and relatively inexpensive; however, its production is energy intensive. Producing one ton of Portland cement—one of the primary ingredients of concrete—consumes about 6.5 million BTUs of energy and releases about one ton of carbon dioxide into the atmosphere. The concrete used in Desert Rain contains 40 percent fly ash, which is the particulate matter captured by pollution control equipment from the smokestacks of coal-burning plants. Using fly ash in this manner diverts the material from the landfill and reduces the amount of Portland cement in the mix—and thereby the amount of energy required to produce the same volume of concrete. Concrete containing fly ash is also stronger and less porous than standard concrete, and shows excellent water tightness; however, it also requires longer set times and can be more brittle. For this reason, the cistern lid was poured with concrete that does not contain fly ash.

In addition to functioning as thermal mass, concrete doubles as the finished floor in the common areas of the main residence (the living room, kitchen and dining room) saving the resources required for additional flooring. Floyd Sapp of Concrete Elegance diamond-polished the floor, which required eight rounds of sanding, starting with 100-grit and working up to 1500 grit. As the surface smoothed, it became more and more reflective. The floor, with its 100-plus-year lifespan, will save resources now and in the future.

The diamond-polished concrete slab in the main residence serves as the finished floor in the kitchen and living rooms.

# THE MOTHER OF INVENTION: STORIES OF INNOVATION

## A LOCAL PLASTER RECIPE

The exterior stucco system on all of the Desert Rain buildings features traditional lime-clay plasters. This choice was driven by the desire to use a material with lower embodied energy.

Only in the last century has Portland cement replaced lime as the binder in plaster recipes. However, Portland cement is characterized by high-embodied energy, whereas lime plasters actually sequester carbon, nearly making up for the carbon dioxide emitted during the lime slaking process. As the stucco material cures and hardens, lime (calcium hydroxide) takes up carbon dioxide from the air and changes into limestone (calcium carbonate). Lime plaster

is a classically beautiful material that naturally resists mold and bacteria growth. It is also breathable, ensuring unwanted moisture does not become trapped inside walls.

Though lime plasters offer compelling environmental benefits, dry mixes were not regionally available. Consequently, David Kaiser, Jr. of Elite Plastering came up with a unique formula using all local and regional ingredients: pumice sand and aggregates from Deschutes River Woods, clay from Prineville, and lime from Washington State. Kaiser and his crew mixed the plaster in pits dug at the Desert Rain site.

# REGIONAL VENDORS, LOCAL CRAFTSPEOPLE

While a custom home project often provides an opportunity for local craftspeople to shine, the Living Building Challenge Material Imperatives ensured Desert Rain is a showcase for regional materials and local craftsmen and artists.

For some, it was also an opportunity to stretch their skills and expand their knowledge. Gabriel Dansky, who made the custom cabinets, became an FSC-certified cabinetmaker so he could participate in this and other Living Building Challenge projects.

The NatureCast sinks and countertops represent another example of thoughtful use of regional materials paired with beautiful craftsmanship. These elements are made from concrete sprayed into a mold over recycled expanded polystyrene foam. The strong, lightweight countertops use a fraction of the concrete compared to solid concrete countertops, and the process virtually eliminates waste.

When sourcing interior products and materials, Wendy Knight deliberately looked to smaller vendors that were growing their product lines. These venders included a small company in California that provided several plumbing fixtures. She and tile-setter Doug Cahail sourced tile from another California company, called Fireclay, which specializes in tile made from mostly recycled materials. The "Crush" tile that forms the backsplash in the bathroom is made from 100 percent recycled waste window glass, sourced from within twenty miles of the company's San Jose factory. Tile for the kitchen backsplash is made from 70 percent recycled content, including crushed porcelain toilets.

*The Materials Petal:* **CONSIDERING THE WHOLE LIFE CYCLE**

River Roofing of Bend fashioned fascia and other elements of the roofing and gutter system onsite. The roofing here is pictured before the snowguards, designed to catch and hold snow, were installed.

# SLEUTHING THE ROOFING

The roof is an important component of any building. It forms the first line of defense against the elements, and the choice of material can affect the building's ability to absorb or reflect heat. At Desert Rain, the roofing structure plays two additional, critical roles. It supports the solar thermal and solar PV arrays, and captures rain and snow—the source of all of the domestic water used on-site.

In addition to complying with the Living Building Challenge Materials Petal criteria, the roofing had to comply with the Oregon Plumbing code, as an approved material for collecting rainwater for potable use.

The team considered copper and zinc, but the cost was prohibitive. Team members ultimately settled on standing-seam steel panels. Rain and snow flow smoothly off steel roofs without absorbing chemicals from the roof itself, and the material is also long-lasting and recyclable. Steel does contain high-embodied energy, as the manufacturing process is energy intensive, but nearly all steel includes some recycled content.

Vetting the material required collaboration and patience. River Roofing of Bend sourced rolls of steel that originated from the East Coast. From there the material traveled from Nevada for forming, then to a plant in Kaluma, Washington, where the coating was applied. First, Vidas determined that the coating on the metal was Red List compliant. Next, the team had to confirm that it met the Oregon Plumbing Code

rules for rainwater collection, which stipulate that rainwater for potable use cannot be collected off a painted roof.

"We had to determine that the manufacturer's applied coating did not equate to a painted coating," says Vidas. "That involved a series of conversations with the Oregon Chief Plumbing Inspector."

Finally, Vidas vetted the steel for the Appropriate Sourcing Imperative, which requires metal elements to come from Zone 1. Since the Standard considers only the distance from the building site to the last manufacturing location, the material complied.

Vidas consulted with River Roofing on the solder used in the joints. Solder contains lead, which is not only a Red List item but could compromise the health of potable water collected off roofs. In the end, the roofing panels and fascia were fabricated in their Bend factory, but the roof ridge and gutters were fabricated on-site to eliminate any joints; thus, there was no need for solder.

# IMPERATIVE:
# CONSERVATION + REUSE: CLOSING THE LOOP

**Construction typically generates tremendous waste. According to the National Association of Home Builders (NAHB), the average 2000-square-foot home generates 8000 pounds, or 50 cubic yards of waste.**

According to Greenwaste.com, home construction, remodeling and demolition projects create 25 to 30 percent of the nation's annual municipal solid waste. Scraps of lumber, drywall and packaging account for much of the refuse.

The final Imperative under the Materials Petal sets purposefully high standards for diverting waste from landfills during the construction phase (see chart on right).

Anna Vacca organized the recycling effort at Desert Rain. Instead of loading refuse into a project dumpster, crews separated waste materials into piles on-site. Vacca picked up the materials with her trailer and delivered them to Deschutes Recycling and the Knott Landfill. As of March 2014, the Desert Rain project had generated just 3,140 pounds of waste for the landfill—about two full dump trailers.

Diverted materials included 22,400 pounds (fifty-six cubic yards) of wood, brush and other compostables, 580 pounds of cardboard, sixty pounds of metal and twenty pounds of mixed paper. In addition, 825 cubic yards of excavated rock— approximately 1238 tons—were taken to a local processing quarry and crushed. Some of this gravel was returned to the site.

In addition, the Conservation + Reuse Imperative instructs project teams to create a conservation plan that optimizes the use of materials through every phase of the project, from design to construction, from operation to end of life. This initiative includes choosing durable materials and products that will endure and that can be easily repurposed or recycled, plus the hiring of craftspeople who value quality and therefore pay attention to details that will ensure the integrity of the buildings for decades to come.

*"The hardest part about recycling on a construction site is getting all of the subcontractors on board. They have to get used to doing it, just like we all had to get used to recycling at home. I labeled all of the cans and the dump trailer; still, I had to sort a lot of it myself at first. It's time consuming, but totally worth it."*

**ANNA VACCA**

According to Anna Vacca, who coordinated the recycling effort at Desert Rain, recycling on the jobsite is largely a matter of habit.

| MATERIAL | MINIMUM DIVERTED (BY WEIGHT) |
|---|---|
| Metals | 95% |
| Paper/Cardboard | 95% |
| Soil/Biomass | 100% |
| Rigid Foam, Carpet, Insulation | 90% |
| All Other (Combined Weighted Average) | 80% |

131

*The Materials Petal:* **CONSIDERING THE WHOLE LIFE CYCLE**

*"The name of our proper connection to the earth is "good work," for good work involves much giving of honor. It honors the source of its materials; it honors the place where it is done; it honors the art by which it is done; it honors the thing that it makes and the user of the made thing."*

WENDELL BERRY

# MATERIAL MINDFULNESS

**The construction industry is notoriously conservative, and understandably so: the conventional economic model dictates that "time is money." Trying out new building techniques, materials and products implies a learning curve that will likely compromise the project's schedule. The standardization of materials and practices has made the business of building generally predictable and relatively efficient, but this efficiency comes with other costs.**

Together, the Imperatives under the Materials Petal encourage an awareness that is usually absent in the construction industry and elsewhere: of how and where every product is manufactured, the distance it had to travel, its packaging, its function in the building, its lifespan and next incarnation. This mindfulness infected every person who spent time on the Desert Rain project, and was expressed in many ways, from finding ways to repurpose materials, such as the wrapping around the lumber, to diligently separating scrap materials for recycling.

"On this project, you might think twice about delivering three boards out to the job, and the next day, delivering five more," says Nate Morgan, sales representative for Parr Lumber. "Because every time you do that it takes resources, such as fuel, and causes emissions. We're trying to overcome historic mindsets of how construction has been done."

Fagan encouraged everyone who worked on Desert Rain to stay vigilant.

"The vetting process is big, but you also need to make sure that the vetted products are the ones that show up

on the jobsite," says Fagan. Subcontractors knew what was at stake, and questioned materials they were not certain about, whether a tube of caulk or a brand of PEX tubing that had not gone through Vidas' vetting process.

Desert Rain's unconventional design and use of non-standard materials required being able to take extra time to avoid mistakes. "With the different wall heights and non-typical break walls, you can't just jump in and build," says Jason Bozovich, who was part of the framing crew. "You have to research everything, from the walls to the trusses, before you nail a board."

The integrated design process informed the actions of each and everyone involved in the project which highlights an important factor in a building's longevity—and hence its sustainability: craftsmanship. Across the board, the men and women who contributed to Desert Rain brought their experience and integrity to the job. Because of their good work, these Living Buildings will honor the materials that went into their construction for decades to come.

132

*The Materials Petal:* **CONSIDERING THE WHOLE LIFE CYCLE**

# THE EQUITY PETAL

## The Human Element

135

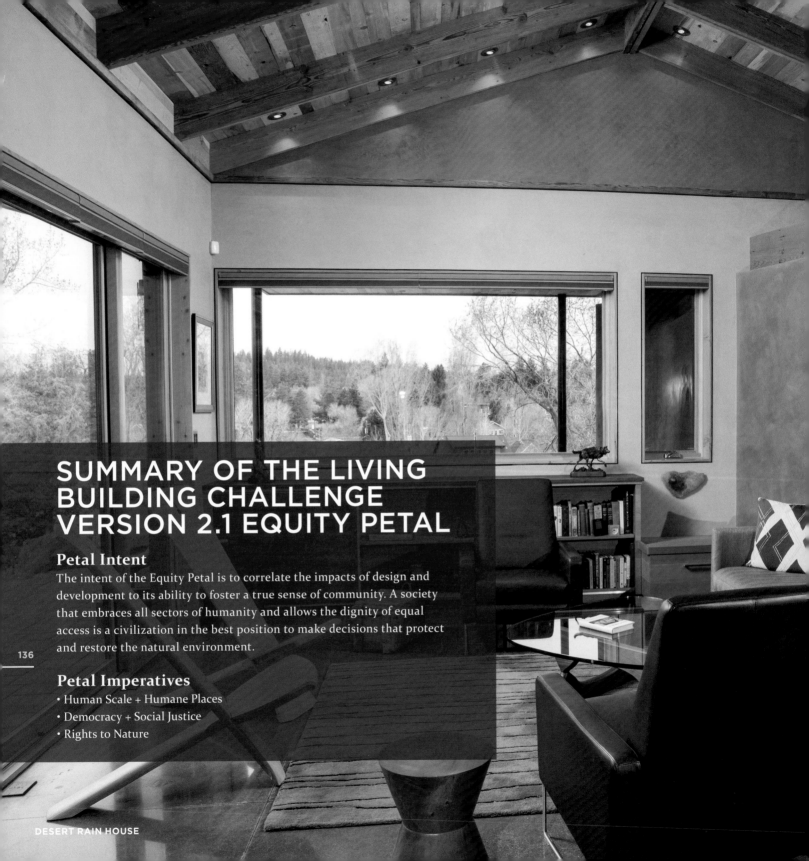

# SUMMARY OF THE LIVING BUILDING CHALLENGE VERSION 2.1 EQUITY PETAL

## Petal Intent

The intent of the Equity Petal is to correlate the impacts of design and development to its ability to foster a true sense of community. A society that embraces all sectors of humanity and allows the dignity of equal access is a civilization in the best position to make decisions that protect and restore the natural environment.

## Petal Imperatives

- Human Scale + Humane Places
- Democracy + Social Justice
- Rights to Nature

> *"There is no question that the environmental movement is most critical to our survival. Our house is literally burning, and it is only logical that environmentalists expect the social justice movement to get on the environmental bus. But it is actually the other way around; the only way we are going to put out this fire is to get on the social justice bus and heal our wounds, because in the end, there is only one bus."*

**PAUL HAWKEN**
from *Blessed Unrest*

# THE EQUITY PETAL: SUPPORTING A JUST, EQUITABLE WORLD

The Equity Petal calls for buildings to contribute to the common good. It urges us to recalibrate our thinking so that we consider the societal impacts of our buildings along with their environmental impacts, which are almost always felt in tandem. The Equity Petal precludes the creation of communities segregated by wealth: exclusive neighborhoods with restricted access to desirable features, such as beaches, versus poor ghettos, which frequently shoulder the burden of environmental degradation and pollution. In contrast, Living Buildings help to create diverse, healthy communities that are accessible to all, regardless of age, income or ability.

## IMPERATIVE:
# HUMAN SCALE + HUMANE PLACES

For too many decades, the automobile culture has dictated design on many scales. The Living Building Challenge recognizes the need to create human-centered communities—spaces that promote culture and interaction, rather than alienate people from each other. This Imperative also outlines specific requirements for the proportion of paved areas and the scale of buildings.

All three residences at Desert Rain fall well under the maximum allowable size of 4,750 square feet; but more importantly, the structures are not out of scale with other buildings in the neighborhood. The site design includes several common areas and opportunities for interaction; in particular, the intersecting pathways, shared food gardens and the area around the constructed wetland. The path that switchbacks up the steep slope from Shasta Place formalizes what was a historic road; benches and native landscaping invite lingering.

No perimeter fence cordons Desert Rain from the rest of the neighborhood, although a short privacy fence rings the central courtyard. Visitors may enter via a welcoming gateless entry. Many details incorporated into the site—the landscaping, the custom gates, the Ponderosa Memorial and images carved into the posts—enhance the visual experience for visitors and neighbors.

The alley access creates a casual, rather than a formal initial experience, and the entrances to the main residence and ADU are adjacent to each other, increasing the possibility of chance interactions between residents of each building. Shared bicycle parking in an enclosed area next to the alley encourages residents to use pedal power for errands and commuting.

The path from Shasta Place to the home site winds up the steep northwest slope to a welcoming patio.

139

Scott and Elliott wheeled their friend Geoff Babb up a makeshift ramp into the main residence while it was under construction, to get his input on making the home more accessible.

140

> *"Much of our standard of living is built on the backs of the less fortunate; for instance, we produce three times the carbon footprint per capita as the rest of the world. The Equity Petal starts to address the inequality of these externalized costs."*
>
> TOM ELLIOTT

IMPERATIVE:
# DEMOCRACY + SOCIAL JUSTICE

**This Imperative states that the project's infrastructure must be accessible to all members of the public. Accessibility in this case is governed largely by the provisions of the Americans with Disabilities Act (ADA). The major pathways on the Desert Rain site are accessible to people with disabilities; both the main residence and ADU include at least one ADA-compliant entry.**

During the framing of the main residence Scott and Elliott invited one of their friends, who uses a wheelchair, to move through the structure so he could advise the couple on ways to improve accessibility. The home's design, with its single story, wide hallways and open plan, facilitates wheelchairs, and the dining table and kitchen island both accommodate wheelchair seating. A few minor additions, such as grab bars in the bathrooms, could easily make the main residence fully accessible.

Scott and Elliott wanted a design that would immediately accommodate their friends and visitors with disabilities, but they were also looking ahead to a time when they themselves might not be as physically mobile. In that event, either Desert Sol or Desert Lookout could potentially function as a caretaker's unit. The smaller suite could also serve as living space for an elderly or disabled person who wanted to remain independent. Noteably, they also expanded their interpretation of the Democracy + Social Justice Imperative to include fair labor practices.

"Equity also refers to the terms of production of materials," says Elliott. Too often, a building project that enhances life for a small group of people degrades it for those others who pay its true cost, whether it is a town exploited by a resource extraction operation or a poor neighborhood cut off from surrounding services by a new highway. The Materials Petal requirements partially address this issue. For instance, the Imperative requires all new lumber to come from sources certified by the Forest Stewardship Council (FSC) ensuring that fair labor practices were employed all along the supply chain. Similarly, the effort to use mostly local materials helps vet materials with regard to Equity. Scott and Elliott had the chance to practice what they preached when it came to dealing with the many people they hired over the course of construction. For instance, when the owner of the company coordinating the deconstruction of the original houses realized his bid was too low, Scott and Elliott worked with him on a revised number that felt fair to all parties.

The concept of fair labor practices has been fully realized in Living Building Challenge Version 3.0; namely, the Just Imperative and associated JUST label, a transparency platform that ensures products are manufactured using fair labor practices.

141

## IMPERATIVE:
# RIGHTS TO NATURE

**A Living Building Challenge project cannot block sunlight, diminish air or water quality or limit access to natural waterways, such as rivers, lakes or coastlines. A formula determines the maximum shade height that a building can cast onto an adjacent façade (based on the sun's angle at the Winter Solstice). Because Desert Rain is a residential compound, the design also had to take into account the effect of buildings on each other within the project boundaries. Working together, Tozer and Hart-Henderson made sure that views were preserved and that each residence enjoys ample daylight.**

The rainwater collection system, constructed wetland, and permeable paved surfaces will all help to minimize stormwater run-off, and the wetland and biological processes in the soil will ensure that stormwater is treated before it percolates into the water table. If anything, Desert Rain will have a positive impact on water quality.

The Rights to Nature Imperative extends beyond the human community. Scott and Elliott hope the Desert Rain grounds will serve as a haven for local urban wildlife, from foraging songbirds to shade-seeking deer. For just as the poor and disenfranchised too often pay the cost for the Western standard of living, fish, frogs and other creatures suffer the price of degraded, diminished or fragmented habitat. Living Buildings serve as models for buildings that serve the common good, enhancing life not only for their residents, but for the larger community—human and otherwise.

143

*The Equity Petal:* **THE HUMAN ELEMENT**

# THE BEAUTY PETAL

## The Nature of Harmony

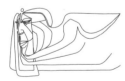

*The Beauty Petal:* **THE NATURE OF HARMONY**

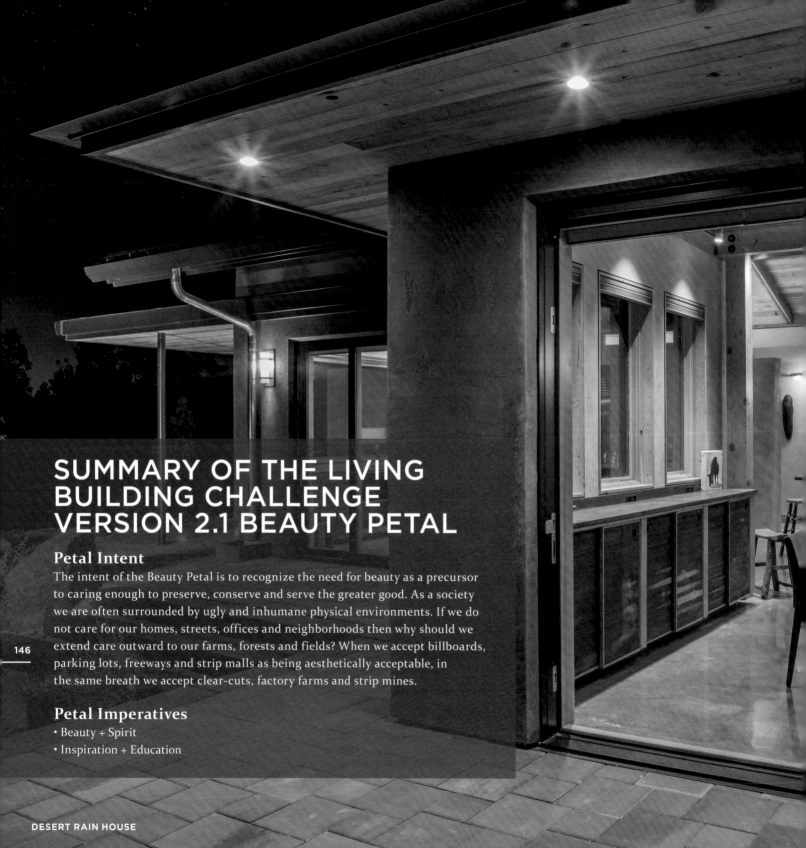

# SUMMARY OF THE LIVING BUILDING CHALLENGE VERSION 2.1 BEAUTY PETAL

## Petal Intent

The intent of the Beauty Petal is to recognize the need for beauty as a precursor to caring enough to preserve, conserve and serve the greater good. As a society we are often surrounded by ugly and inhumane physical environments. If we do not care for our homes, streets, offices and neighborhoods then why should we extend care outward to our farms, forests and fields? When we accept billboards, parking lots, freeways and strip malls as being aesthetically acceptable, in the same breath we accept clear-cuts, factory farms and strip mines.

## Petal Imperatives

• Beauty + Spirit
• Inspiration + Education

# THE BEAUTY PETAL

The deliberate decision to place Beauty on par with Energy and Materials is one of the most intriguing aspects of the Living Building Challenge. The point of this Petal is not to dictate aesthetics; there is no "Beauty Scorecard." Rather, the Petal was conceived in recognition that beauty serves as "a precursor to caring enough to conserve, preserve and serve the greater good." It attempts to gauge intentionality: that care, and even reverence, have imbued every aspect of the project, so that it is not merely an efficient feat of engineering, but a building (or set of buildings) that lifts the spirit and inspires body and mind. There is the implication that as we treat our buildings, so we treat our neighbors, our children, other creatures and the larger landscape. If we build beautiful, inspiring buildings, we will tend to care for them, and ensure that they endure.

Scott and Elliott tell people they embarked on Desert Rain with the intention that the buildings will thrive for at least 200 years. And so there is an element of timelessness to beauty—an assumption that what appeals to us now will still appeal to us centuries later. In this way, nature is a safe bet. We have been copying, modeling, and seeking solace from natural forms and materials for as long as there is evidence of our presence on the earth.

Desert Rain's palette was inspired by the native manzanita, a shrub with beautifully-smooth, dark red bark and greenish-gray leaves, which turn a lovely salmon color as they shed.

## IMPERATIVE:
# BEAUTY + SPIRIT: DELIGHTFUL DETAILS

This Imperative states simply: "The project must contain design features intended solely for human delight and the celebration of culture, spirit and place appropriate to its function."

Scott and Elliott are attracted to architecture that is both warm and modern, but not too refined. It's an aesthetic dominated by earth tones and natural materials like woods and stone that they refer to as "contemporary funk." All of the buildings at Desert Rain reflect this aesthetic, from the stucco exteriors and clay plaster interior walls to the extensive use of wood throughout the house, much of it reclaimed. Often reclaimed lumber is deemed unfit as a finishing material and it is instead "hidden" in structure, but Scott and Elliott chose to showcase much of it; for example, the roof eave soffits are clad with lumber salvaged from the original structures on the property. Though the boards were milled and planed, subtle variations in the thickness of the boards make for a slightly uneven effect.

For Scott and Elliott, knowing the stories behind so many of the materials enhances their beauty. For example, the walnut wood used in some of the countertops and built-ins came from a single tree harvested from the campus of Concordia College in Portland.

"The rest of our lives we will feel a special connection with that walnut, knowing where it came from," says Elliott. The specificity of the materials—and the stories behind them—do not just make the house unique, they create a web of connections that root the buildings in place and time.

Another hallmark of the "contemporary funk" aesthetic is a balance of yin and yang: angular, masculine lines, such as

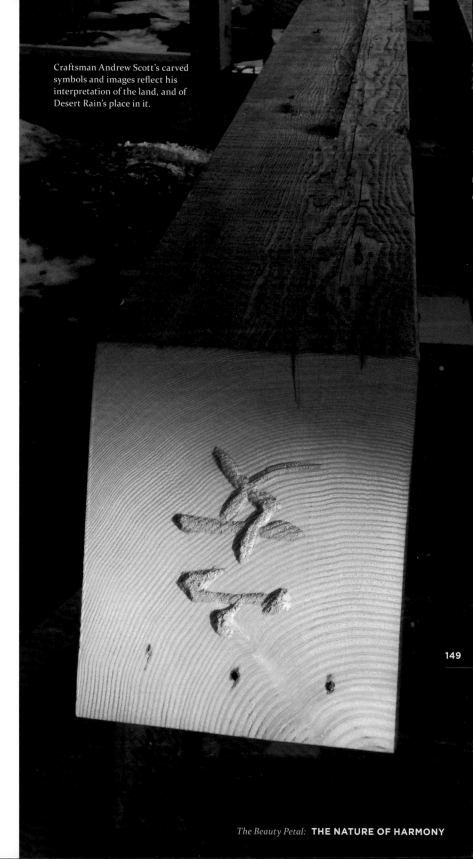

Craftsman Andrew Scott's carved symbols and images reflect his interpretation of the land, and of Desert Rain's place in it.

the counterpointing shed roofs and cube-like volumes, balanced with feminine curves and the earth-toned palette. The Miró Wall, which is also a good example of the intersection of biophilia and beauty, introduces a large curve that unifies the buildings, and is echoed by the curving pathways that wind through the site. Cooler materials like steel, used in posts, roofing and fascia, are balanced by the warmer tones of the stucco and wood. The natural beauty of the native landscaping complements the building aesthetics.

Then there are those details designed into Desert Rain simply because they enhance the experience of being there. These details include niches and sections of blank wall to accommodate original works of art: paintings and sculptures that the couple have collected from local artists as well as from their years in Montana and the Southwest. The custom doors, gates and entry offer a unique experience to anyone who passes through them. The main entry into the central courtyard is an amalgam of a trilithon—an ancient post and lintel gateway—and a traditional Chinese gate. Tozer designed the entry, matching the curve of the top post with the curve of the Miró Wall. Andrew Scott, an acupuncturist, woodworker and friend of Scott and Elliott's, worked with Tozer's design, adding carved characters for harmony and tranquility to the top of the posts. He also added carvings of native wildlife and other nature-inspired symbols to the tops of other gateposts throughout the site—details that will not necessarily be seen, but may be felt.

149

150

# IMPERATIVE:
# INSPIRATION + EDUCATION: CONCENTRIC CIRCLES

This Imperative states that "educational materials about the performance and operation of the project must be made public to share successful solutions and to motivate others to make change," and that the project must be open to the public at least one day per year.

Scott and Elliott conceived Desert Rain as a demonstration project from the beginning; committing to the Living Building Challenge only strengthened that aim. They went about educating as many people as possible from all angles, from the numerous tours conducted on-site to the website created for the project, and finally, to the book you hold in your hands.

Scott and Elliott hosted dozens of tours on-site while Desert Rain was under construction so that by the time they moved into the main residence literally hundreds of people had crossed their threshold. The tours have ranged from public events, such as the region's annual Solar Tour, to private tours for specific groups, including friends and family.

Notable visitors have included Dennis Hayes, founder of Earth Day and CEO of the Bullitt Center in Seattle, another Living Building Challenge project, and his wife, Gail Bryer-Hayes. Living Building Challenge founder Jason F. McLennan also toured Desert Rain along with various other staff members of the International Living Future Institute.

"We've had VIPs, but just as importantly, we have classes from Highland Elementary, the local school, or people who have just given me their names," says Scott, who keeps a running list of people who have requested a tour.

In 2012, Timberline Construction hosted Green Drinks, a bimonthly sustainability and networking event sponsored by The Environmental Center, at Desert Rain. Several school groups toured the site, including a group from Highland Elementary and seventh-graders from Powell Butte Charter School. River Bend School teacher Jen Goodman included Desert Rain in a chapter on sustainability; her junior high school students toured the site and enjoyed an in-class presentation from Living Building Challenge Ambassador and sustainable design consultant ML Vidas.

Some groups visited Desert Rain to gain practical knowledge. Students with the Clean Energy Service Corps, which partners with Habitat for Humanity on its affordable housing projects, visited Desert Rain to learn about different types of insulation and installation techniques.

Desert Rain House was part of the Central Oregon Solar Tour two years in a row. Hosted by the High Desert Branch of the Cascadia Green Building Council, the annual fall tour draws an average of 700 participants. In 2013, tour-goers honored Desert Rain with the People's Choice award which recognizes the residential project with the most sustainable features and positive impact on the community.

Scott and Elliott have also taught classes at Central Oregon Community College (COCC), and hope to work with students on an ongoing project to track and analyze data from Desert Rain's monitoring systems.

Scott and Vidas lead a small tour group of students on one of many tours held during Desert Rain's construction.

151

*"Let the beauty of what you love be
what you do. There are a thousand
ways to kneel and kiss the earth."*

RUMI

# A COMMITMENT TO TRANSPARENCY

Early on, an editor from The Bulletin, Bend's
primary newspaper, approached Scott and
Elliott about covering the project in a series
of newspaper articles, so long as they agreed
to be open about everything, including the
project's budget and actual cost. Recognizing
the opportunity to expose a large number of
people to the Living Building Challenge—
the printed paper enjoys a circulation
of over 25,000—the couple agreed.

The first article, titled "Let's just go extreme" and written
by Erin Golden, was published on October 11, 2009. Photo
editor Dean Guernsey chronicled the project with images,
and business reporter Rachael Rees wrote many of the
twenty-plus articles. Though she had always been passionate
about educating others about green technology, Rees says
learning so much about a single project was "eye-opening."

"It made me question, why aren't other building [projects] doing
some of these things?" Because the articles covered the project as
it unfolded, Rees and the other journalists were able to capture
dramatic events, such as the approval of the greywater wetland
and the decision to scrap the original design in favor of a new one
that incorporated the Living Building Challenge. As the project
progressed—and as its cost crept up—the articles no doubt
sparked conversations in living rooms and cafes all across town.

152

The Bulletin, Bend's primary newspaper, published a series of articles chronicling Desert Rain's progress. Photographer Dean Guernsey captured the project in pictures.

# REACHING BEYOND BEND: DESERT RAIN BLOGGERS

**In 2011, Scott and Elliott created a website to chronicle the construction of Desert Rain. Along with information about the Living Building Challenge and links to The Bulletin articles, the "meat" of the website is its very active blog, which has been maintained by three different bloggers.**

Tina Davis entered the first posts in early 2012; Kelly Riley took over late that spring. Riley, a musician with a background in environmental design, was referred to Scott and Elliott through Chris Hart-Henderson, for whom she had worked. Riley took on the task with a mandate: to write about Desert Rain from the perspective of a non-expert. Over the next year and a half she wrote detailed weekly posts, covering everything from the custom plaster recipe to the ongoing quest for approval of the greywater system. She supplemented her posts with photos and research and enlivened them with quotes, having interviewed nearly every person who came on-site to work on the project.

"Everyone had something to teach, and a story to tell," says Riley, who now works for Sunlight Solar Energy in Bend.

In July 2014, Sweet Pea Cole took over the blog. The artist, freelance marketer and self-described "mountain girl" had worked as the office manager for Timberline Construction, so she was familiar with the project from the contractor's perspective. She also knew Tom Elliott through his service on the board of the Environmental Center, where she had previously worked. Like her predecessors, Cole chooses topics based on what is happening with the project and who she can connect with on the team, aiming to make complicated, technical aspects of green building understandable. Writing about Desert Rain confirmed an early observation about her adopted city.

"There's a collaborative spirit in Bend, and it just keeps getting stronger," she says, adding that "this creates a ripe environment for a Living Building Challenge project."

153

# A SIGN OF SOMETHING SPECIAL

**As their project broke ground, Scott and Elliott wanted the chance to educate even casual passers-by about the Living Building Challenge, so they decided to post signs on both entrances to the site.**

Barbara Scott's brother, Kevin Scott, had been following the project. "I wanted to help in some way, so I said, I can make one of the signs." Though a tool and die maker by trade, he has crafted fine furniture all of his life. Kevin consulted with Barbara and Tom on the text and architectural drawings; signage was to include information about the Living Building Challenge Petals, a description of Desert Rain and a simple elevation drawing. Scott designed and built the sign in his shop in Colorado, planing and sanding raw maple planks, and joining them with stainless steel fins. He formed the letters and drawing using a CNC router (computer controlled cutting machine), carefully arranging them so they would not overlap where the planks joined each other, and finished the sign with a material that complied with Living Building Challenge criteria. Once it was complete, Kevin Scott took the sign apart, flew with it to Oregon and reassembled it on-site; a local welder made the sign frame.

The sign stood on the western slope of the property near the street throughout construction; more recently, it was incorporated into a privacy fence. With over one hundred hours invested, the sign is a reflection of the care and attention to detail seen throughout the Desert Rain project.

# EDUCATING
# THE EXPERTS

**None of the core Desert Rain team members had been previously involved in a Living Building Challenge project. By the time construction wrapped up, all of the team members had become experts.**

Even if they do not work on another Living Building, the experience will no doubt inform their best practices. Tozer says he would consider another Living Building Challenge project "in a heartbeat."

"We would be so much better prepared to educate someone who is considering a Living Building Challenge project." To that end, Scott and Elliott are considering a second project, with an equally ambitious goal: to build a "market-rate" Living Building.

The ripple effect of Desert Rain extends far beyond the core team. Scott and Elliott required every person who worked on the project to attend a one-hour presentation on the Living Building Challenge, which ensured that all sub-contractors understood their vision.

"A lot of people got to work on this project," says Fagan. "Some of the guys grumbled [about the presentations] at first, but it generated a lot of questions, and people took ownership of the project instead of just being told, 'this is what you're going to do.'"

By their nature, Living Building Challenge projects push boundaries and challenge the status quo. Demonstrating that a new or unconventional technique or material can persuade skeptics (or the merely cautious) to consider advanced approaches. At Desert Rain, the constructed wetland, rainwater harvesting system and blackwater system were all firsts for a residential project in an urban setting.

These innovative systems have the potential to become extremely influential, says Morgan Brown. "They will be a vehicle for valuable study; others will want to emulate them, and finally, that will make it more affordable for those that follow."

Though the process was frustrating, working with representatives from the City of Bend and the State of Oregon exposed people

Scott and Elliott do not expect every system to work perfectly— or exactly as planned. But the function of a demonstration project is to find out what works, as well as what does not, in hopes that the next iteration will improve upon it.

with some regulatory power to both the general concepts of the Living Building Challenge and to specific alternative solutions for servicing a home with potable water and treating wastewater. Now that the constructed wetland has been approved, for example, it will serve as a tangible demonstration for how such a wetland can work in an urban setting.

Brown and ML Vidas gave a presentation titled "Lessons on the Bleeding Edge" at the 2013 Living Future Unconference, which focused on the challenges related to local approval of these ground-breaking systems; Scott and Elliott participated with them in a round-table discussion afterwards. In this way, builders, architects, consultants and other professionals gained valuable advice for working around the challenges they are sure to encounter in their own projects. The following year Brown, Scott, Elliott and Vidas took part in another education session, titled "Great Adaptations: Living Building Challenge Solutions at Desert Rain and Gaddy House."

Scott and Elliott plan to take the "lessons learned" and directly apply them to a new project, which they're calling "LBC Lite": a market-rate Living Building. While they will undoubtedly work with many of the same people who collaborated on Desert Rain, they will also deliberately recruit professionals who have not worked on a Living Building Challenge project before, thus widening the circle of experience.

155

# A BROADER DEFINITION

In November 2014, Elliott and Scott received the Pioneer Award from the Environmental Center in Bend. Upon accepting the award, Elliott asked audience members who had participated in some aspect of the Desert Rain project to raise their hands.

"There was a collective gasp at the number of raised hands," says Elliott. It was a poignant moment for the couple, as they reflected on how many people their project has touched.

The question of beauty has occupied human beings through the centuries. What exactly defines beauty? And are there qualities that make a thing or phenomenon universally beautiful? While many might agree that Desert Rain represents a set of materially beautiful, well-integrated buildings, and while the systems in their elegance represent another kind of beauty, the project's truest beauty stems from a quality shared with other breathtaking phenomena, from symphonies and cathedrals to forests and coral reefs. While at first glance these may seem very different examples of beauty, each is the result of a collaborative, creative act, and it is the act as much as the result that is beautiful.

In some ways the Beauty Petal is the most important one. If a Living Building Challenge project were to happen in a vacuum, if no one knew about it, why would it matter? The true Imperative here is not just to perpetuate the Living Building Challenge, but the spirit behind it; the act of creating something greater than the sum of its parts; something which benefits the common good. Thanks to the multi-pronged efforts of the Desert Rain team, and the hundreds of people who have encountered the project, either in passing or as an integral part of the story, its influence—its beauty—will continue to radiate outward.

156

# AMBASSADOR FOR CHANGE:
# MARY LOUISE (ML) VIDAS

ML Vidas became an Ambassador for the Living Building Challenge while consulting on the Desert Rain project. As part of the commitment, she must give a minimum of six free presentations per year. While Vidas often presents to groups of professionals, some of her audiences have been groups from the community, including her parents' retirement community.

"Over fifty people came; most of the audience was 80-plus years old," she recalls. "But they were just as interested as architects and subcontractors. It was so exciting to see these people—who are nearing the end of their lives—so concerned about our future."

Vidas embraces the collaborative nature of Living Building Challenge projects, and she would love to work with another team. For her, it did not matter that she did not get to control the design; instead, she focused on vetting materials and serving as the hub for information.

"The training of architecture is about problem-solving," she says. "Going into a situation where there is this chaos of information and sorting it out; helping people make better decisions. To me, that's what design is."

# PART IV

*Propagation*

Using the Desert Rain Experience to
Expand the Living Building Challenge

160

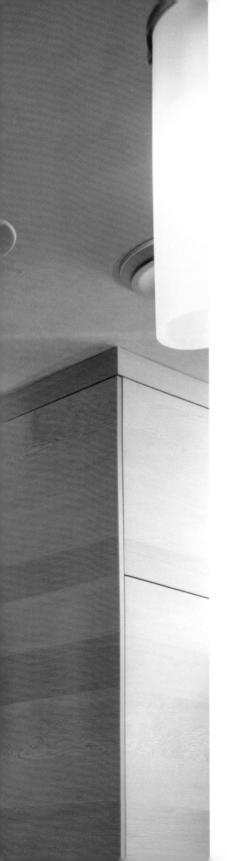

*"What is it worth to involve dozens of local trades in the construction of the world's first residence to meet the Living Building Challenge? What is it worth to have that knowledge ripple out into the community through their respective efforts? What is it worth to blaze the trail in terms of design and regulatory hurdles to make it easier for the next generation of green homes to be built? What value do we assign to the hundreds of students and others who have toured this project and picked up maybe one new idea or a small inspiration that could change the course of their lives? What is it worth to live in a healthy environment and to model that form of building for future generations? What is it worth to eliminate externalized costs instead of passing those on to our children and grandchildren?"*

TOM ELLIOTT AND BARB SCOTT

# PROPAGATION

**By January of 2015, nearly six years after Tom Elliott and Barb Scott decided to build their "extreme, green dream," and five years after they committed to the Living Building Challenge, construction on Desert Lookout, the project's final building, drew to a close. As the construction dust settled, Scott and Elliott began reflecting on what they had accomplished, and they began looking ahead to how to apply the many lessons they and the rest of the team had learned.**

From the beginning, Scott was clear about her motives. "We don't want to build Desert Rain and be done," she says. "We believe in the Living Building Challenge and we feel it is our responsibility to propagate building with these guidelines."

Just as Scott and Elliott took advantage of every educational opportunity while the project was under construction, now that the project is complete they continue to find ways to educate others whether through collaborative initiatives with the local community college, or by hosting workshops and other events at the Desert Rain site. They are also considering directly applying the lessons learned from

Desert Rain in a new project aimed at creating a more affordable Living Building.

Evaluating the performance of Desert Rain's many systems will inform new projects. While Desert Rain's audit year has not officially begun, Scott and Elliott have started monitoring the project's systems. They hired Powers of Automation, a Bend-based company that specializes in systems for the biotech and high-tech industries, to develop the sophisticated control and monitoring system. Owner Steve Powers consulted with Morgan Brown of Whole Water Systems to develop the water-related aspects, and worked with All Phase Electric Services on the installation.

161

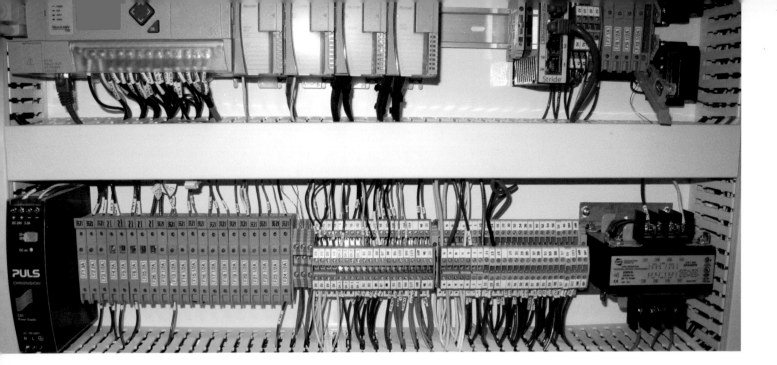

The scope of the control and monitoring system far exceeds what is usually seen in residential applications. It includes the rainwater, greywater, composting and energy systems. A screen interface at the main garage panel allows Scott and Elliott to check on any of these; they can also access data remotely from their computer. Here are the system's highlights:

## RAINWATER SYSTEM

A flow meter measures the flow of rainwater, and a continuous level sensor monitors the cistern level. The city water valve is set to open when the cistern reaches a certain low level, and shuts off once the water level exceeds the cistern's threshold. The failure of various components—a pump or the UV treatment system, for example—triggers an alarm.

## GREYWATER SYSTEM

A float-activated sump pump sends effluent from the primary greywater tank to the wetland, and a flow sensor monitors the flow. Both greywater storage tanks include level sensors and high level floats; a flow sensor monitors the flow of greywater from the first storage tank to the second tank. The primary greywater tank feeds the irrigation system, which includes a single pump and five programmable zones. The failure of any of the pumps triggers an alarm, as will too-low or too-high levels in the storage tanks.

## COMPOSTING SYSTEM

Sensors monitor levels in the composting chamber and evaporating chamber; high levels in either part trigger an alarm. The vacuum toilet system is monitored for the number of starts—the number of toilet flushes—and for failure.

## ENERGY SYSTEM

Web-based software monitors the energy production from the solar PV array and the consumption from various individual and grouped sources. For instance, Scott and Elliott can track how much energy is being consumed by car charging, greywater pumps or lighting in the main residence. Sensors also monitor the temperatures to and from the solar water collectors, and in the heat pump's heat exchanger.

## WEATHER STATION

A weather system monitors temperature, barometric pressure, dewpoint, relative humidity, rainfall, and wind speed and wind direction.

## OVERFLOW TO SANITARY SEWER

Both the greywater storage tank and the composting system connect to Bend's sanitary sewer. A single flow switch monitors effluent flow from the Desert Rain property to the sanitary sewer, and triggers an alarm along with text and email notifications.

*"Externalized costs are those created by an industry but paid for by society as a whole. In the construction industry, these include things like stormwater runoff, pollution from hazardous waste, and noise pollution. These are often "out of sight, out of mind," but represent very real costs to the community as a whole. Ethically, it is unjust to impose external costs on people and communities that do not share in the profits of the activity."*

TOM ELLIOTT

# THE ELEPHANT IN THE ROOM

**When all was said and done, the Desert Rain project, including the deconstruction of the original building and salvaging of materials, the design and construction of five new structures, landscaping, design, engineering and installation of the various systems, including the solar PV and solar thermal arrays, constructed wetland, rainwater cistern, composting system and associated pipes, pumps and monitoring systems, cost $3.48 million.**

This total works out to a construction cost of $638 per square foot. No matter how you look at it, these numbers put the project far out of reach of most homeowners—something Scott and Elliott readily acknowledge.

"We struggle with the overall cost of this project," says Elliott. "Barb and I do not live an extravagant lifestyle; we don't own a yacht or a corporate jet. What we value most is our family, our community of friends and the opportunity to hike, bike and ski."

When they agreed to allow *The Bulletin* to publish a series of articles on their project, including total transparency about its cost, they knew they were opening themselves up to criticism.

"We know we are blessed," says Scott. "And we have chosen to put our money into this project instead of something else."

Three factors drove up costs for Desert Rain. Minimizing externalized costs—those that industry passes to society as a whole in the form of pollution, degraded environments and exploited labor—meant the project more accurately reflects the true cost of building. Secondly, navigating the uncharted territory of the Living Building Challenge meant going down roads that led to dead ends, which drove up the cost of design. Finally, for many of Desert Rain's cutting-edge systems, a good proportion of the budget went to so-called "soft costs": design and development, research, materials vetting, meetings and engineering.

163

## DESERT RAIN SYSTEMS COST BREAKDOWN

| | |
|---|---|
| Photovoltaic System | $64,678.00 |
| Solar Thermal System | $30,729.00 |
| Rainwater Harvesting and Treatment System | $74,680.33 |
| Greywater Treatment System | $26,051.09 |
| Blackwater Treatment System | $49,019.22 |
| System Controls and Monitoring | $58,013.30 |
| Systems Design and Regulatory Costs | $142,157.35 |
| **TOTAL SYSTEMS COSTS** | **$445,328.29** |

Scott and Elliott take solace in knowing that their pioneering work will reduce these costs for future projects. They have also concluded that some of the solutions the Desert Rain team found, especially to meet the Water Petal requirements, simply are not practical for single-family residences, or even small residential compounds, and may be more suitable on the scale of a neighborhood or multi-family building. This is where the notion of scale-jumping could be applied. Recognizing that the appropriate scale, environmental impact and burden of cost may instruct a system to fall outside the project boundary, the Living Building Challenge allows multiple projects to share infrastructure, be it a solar array, rainwater cistern or wastewater treatment system.

"What we did at Desert Rain for wastewater just isn't the right scale," says Vidas. "We need to think about clustering buildings together and sharing resources. We need to start asking, where is the tipping point? How many homes?"

Now that Desert Rain has "broken in" several pioneering systems, including Oregon's first permitted Tier II greywater system, future teams will undoubtedly face many fewer obstacles to regulatory approval in the future. Though Scott and Elliott understand that this is one of their project's biggest contributions, they are not satisfied to stop there.

Midway through the process, as they saw Desert Rain's costs escalating, they began thinking ahead to their next project: a market-rate or even affordable Living Building Challenge home or cluster of homes they dubbed "LBC Lite." Through strategies gleaned from the sometimes painful lessons learned at Desert Rain, they believe they can bring the costs to under $200 per square foot—a competitive rate for the Bend market. These strategies include simplified design and construction, shared infrastructure, and taking advantage of the "broken-in" code and expertise of local subcontractors who have already worked on a Living Building Challenge project.

# LESSONS LEARNED: ADVICE FOR OTHER BRAVE PIONEERS

**As more Living Building Challenge projects near completion, the pool of resources for new project teams grows. More types of projects are breaking ground in every region; the matrix is filling in. In time, the number of Living Buildings will reach critical mass, and achieving Living Building Challenge standards will no longer be a challenge, but the norm. Such is the vision.**

In the meantime, as one of the first residential projects striving for full certification, Desert Rain has much to offer other project teams embarking on a residential construction project. The Desert Rain team offers these words of encouragement and advice for other brave pioneers who are passionate about creating truly sustainable, regenerative buildings and communities.

## ASSEMBLE A QUALITY AND COMMITTED TEAM

Knowledge and experience is important, but so is the genuine willingness to collaborate with others. Look for passion and heart along with a strong portfolio, and beware of controlling personalities and big egos. Collaboration fosters accountability, says Scott. "Everyone has to sit at the same table, even if each team member has a different role," she says. "They are accountable to each other."

Interview each of your team members carefully, and look for a contractor with the personality to handle the uncertainties associated with a cutting-edge project.

## MAKE IT PERSONAL

Scott and Elliott found ways to ensure each team member was aligned with the goals of the Living Building Challenge. This strategic approach included requiring every person who worked on the Desert Rain project to attend a presentation on the Living Building Challenge and sign a compliance agreement. In addition to encouraging team members to embrace the Challenge, Scott and Elliott created an atmosphere where people could learn without their egos getting in the way.

"We decided yes, let's give a presentation on the Living Building Challenge, but let's include who we are at a personal level, and communicate that we want to know who you are on a personal level, too," says Scott. She and Elliott took time to meet with the team informally, often at the dinner table, and discussed what was important to each person philosophically, before getting down to the business of the project itself.

**165**

> *"Don't believe the adage that you are embarking on a path to potential divorce. Make your marriage number one because in the end, it is only a house. Take time each day to set the intention about who is doing what and who is communicating with who. Realize that you are different and approach things differently—draw upon each other's strengths."*

**BARB SCOTT**, on taking on a project as a couple

## INDIVIDUALS MATTER

One person can play a critical role in either hindering or helping a project team overcome an obstacle. It is important to remember that, in most cases, people in positions of regulatory power are simply trying to do their jobs well and avoid setting precedents that lead to unwanted consequences. If a person is showing resistance to an aspect of your project that is in uncharted territory or subject to different interpretations, do not assume they are thwarting you just because they can. Communication is key. In the first case, careful strategizing will pay off. Take the extra time to discuss how to best approach this person and "win" him or her over to your side.

This is not to say that there are not situations in which political pressure is an option. "Future Living Building Challenge projects hoping to break new ground with regulatory codes should consider lining up this political support in advance," suggests Brown. "History has shown that this step is often necessary."

The Desert Rain team considered using such a strategy when it had reached an impasse regarding the constructed wetland as a pretreatment system, and the Bend Building Division Manager suddenly inserted himself in the process. Ultimately, the team decided not to go that route; instead, the team sought approval for the system under Oregon's new greywater code.

## BE PREPARED TO EDUCATE THE EXPERTS

Government officials or people with regulatory power do not always have the answers, especially if they are navigating a newer regulation or code that has never been tested. Sometimes officials simply need reassurance about the proposed interpretation. Find ways to instill confidence in your preferred interpretation, and be prepared with tangible examples, especially if there are local or regional examples. Find a colleague or someone from another agency to assist in educating them.

The Desert Rain team found such ambassadors in Oregon State Chief Plumbing Inspector Terry Swisher and code specialist Tim Lindsey, who helped interpret Oregon's rainwater collection guidelines. Once Swisher and Lindsey expressed confidence in the Desert Rain team's interpretation of these guidelines—both verbally and in writing—the local officials accepted the recommendations.

## EMBRACE THE NOTION OF "SLOW BUILD"

A Living Building Challenge project is going to take longer to complete. Working with a team always requires more time, simply because there are more schedules and opinions to consider. Allow extra time for researching, vetting materials, designing (and redesigning) innovative systems and working through bureaucratic obstacles, keeping in mind that it is more important to do something correctly than to stay on schedule.

## UNDERSTAND THE RISKS

Building on the "bleeding edge" is fraught with risks. This uncharted territory often breeds start-ups and companies that may not enjoy the stability of more established firms. Scott and Elliott originally awarded the contract for system controls and monitoring to a company that was not able to deliver the required services, and which went out of business after they had spent several thousand dollars on design and installed equipment.

An "unconventional" project may subvert the usual sequence of events. At Desert Rain, many outdoor plumbing and wastewater lines were not installed until after the structure was built—a reversal of the norm. Scott and Elliott decided to install 1.5" plumbing lines leading from the bathrooms to the central composting chamber that could accommodate vacuum toilets, just in case they decided to install them later. Eventually, they did receive approval for the vacuum toilets and evaporator/ composting chamber, but the toilets they had originally chosen were not adequate. The Jets toilets they ultimately sourced required 2" waste lines. They had no choice but to dig up the installed lines and replace them with the 2" lines.

"That's the contractor's nightmare," says Fagan. "You're always guessing."

## HONEST MISTAKES HAPPEN; LEARN FROM THEM

For example, Brown and biologist John Grove persuaded Scott and Elliott to use local cinder rock to fill the constructed wetland. Not only was the red rock a better match aesthetically, they believed it would support a more robust colony of bacteria, which help clean the effluent entering the wetland. Scott and Elliott agreed to try it, but once the cinder was in place, they realized it contained too many fine particles to work effectively. Ultimately, the cinder rock had to be removed.

## BEWARE OF BURN-OUT

A residential project comes with particular challenges. Homeowners are usually not accustomed to the construction schedule—including the inevitable delays— and have little experience making the literally hundreds of decisions that are required. Sometimes the homeowners are living on-site during the project, making it difficult for them to escape from the state of construction.

Scott and Elliott stress the importance of taking breaks and leaving the site, even if only for a few days. Ironically, pursuing

an ideal that results in a healthy building and quality of life can take a toll on mental and physical well-being. Take time to eat well, sleep and exercise, and to enjoy yourself, family and friends.

## SET LIMITS

Scott and Elliott admit Desert Rain suffered from "feature creep," to the extent that they added a whole new building—Desert Lookout—late in the process.

"We were dealing with huge unknowns, and were willing to persist more than others would, both in terms of time and money," says Elliott. But this does not mean everyone else can or should follow this example. Scott and Elliott emphasize the need to define the scope of work and the budget, and to use this information to make difficult decisions.

## KNOW YOUR STRENGTHS AND WEAKNESSES

A construction project will test you and your relationships. If you know you have trouble making decisions, consider delegating some of them to someone you trust. If you hire experts, there will be times you will need to get out of the way and trust them to do their jobs. On the other hand, it is important to step in early if you notice the schedule sliding or the budget spiraling out of control.

## ENJOY THE RIDE

A Living Building Project is a journey and an adventure. No matter how well you prepare, obstacles and frustrations will arise. Holding fast to the vision will help you persevere, says Scott. "There are certain things you can't know until you're in it."

167

**Even if a project team decides it cannot pursue full or even partial Living Building Challenge certification, team members can still do much to achieve the spirit of the program. Here are Scott and Elliott's "top ten" recommendations.**

**SITING.** Passive solar orientation and the proper placement of windows can reduce a building's heating and cooling demand, enhance its comfort and aesthetics, and connect the building to the landscape.

**FORTIFIED ENVELOPE.** Building a tighter home with more insulation will reduce heating and cooling energy demand and increase the home's comfort. If you are building a wood-framed home, advanced framing techniques will reduce thermal bridging and increase the envelope's performance, at little, if any, increased cost. In fact, many of these techniques will reduce the amount of lumber used. Attention to air-sealing will ensure the insulation performs to its potential, and high-performance windows will pay for themselves over time in energy saved.

**CERTIFIED LUMBER.** Using lumber certified by the Forest Stewardship Council will increase the cost of your project by 10 to 15 percent. Using reclaimed or salvaged lumber will minimize the carbon impact of wood materials, but because the costs are not externalized, expect to pay more for it than conventional lumber or certified lumber.

**EFFICIENT HVAC.** The efficiencies of heating and cooling equipment have improved dramatically. From mini-split heat pumps to geothermal units, there is a solution for every size and type of building. The initial investment in high-performance equipment will pay off for years to come.

**DOWNSIZING.** Building a smaller home may be the greenest decision you can make. A capable architect or designer can create spaces that perform double duty.

**SIMPLICITY.** A smaller "palette" of materials means less vetting and research. Similarly, choosing structural elements that can serve as finish materials—for example, a concrete slab floor or exposed trusses—save both materials and cost.

**APPROPRIATE LANDSCAPING.** Choosing native or naturalized plants that thrive in the region's climate will reduce irrigation demand. Installing a drip system will ensure the efficient use of water.

**RIGHT LIGHTING.** The quality of LED lamps and fixtures keeps improving, and LEDs are becoming more affordable. Using efficient fixtures will reduce energy demand, as will design that maximizes natural daylighting.

**REUSED MATERIALS.** Finding used and reclaimed materials has never been easier thanks to resources like the Habitat for Humanity Restore and building supply stores that specialize in reclaimed lumber and other materials.

**MODIFY YOUR BEHAVIOR.** Conserving water and energy does not cost anything, and will connect you with your home, site and the larger environment.

"*If you really want to pursue the Living Building Challenge and stay true to the mission, building smaller is a huge part of that. If you're building two-thirds the house, that's less of everything—fewer materials; less transportation; less volume to heat.*"

WENDY KNIGHT

169

# THANKS TO OUR TEAM

"It's sort of like climbing a mountain. It gets steep and difficult at times but you keep your goal in mind, knowing there will be an amazing view up there and a real sense of accomplishment. But I wasn't climbing this mountain alone; I was also inspiring others alongside me. People naturally become less enthused the longer you have to strive for a goal — they need coaching. That's where I came in."

**BARB SCOTT**, on avoiding burn-out and working with a team

*Part IV:* **PROPAGATION**

# LIVING BUILDING PARTNERS

## DESIGN TEAM

Tozer Design

## SUSTAINABILITY AND SYSTEMS DESIGN

Vidas Architecture

Whole Water Systems

Earth Advantage

Powers of Automation

Advanced Composting Systems

Luma Lighting Design

## GENERAL CONTRACTOR

Timberline Construction

## ENGINEERING

Walker Structural Engineering LLC

Elemental Engineering

Pace Engineering

Interface Engineering

## LANDSCAPE DESIGN

Hearts Springs Landscape Design

Winter Creek Restoration

## SUBCONTRACTORS

All Phase Electric Service

American Painting

Andrew Scott Woodworks

Bend Glass & Mirror

Blankenship Garage Doors

Bobcat & Sun

Boxcar Productions

Brian Kennel Custom Milling

Button Up Energy

Cahail Construction

Cascade Pump & Irrigation Services

Cement Elegance

Classic Coverings & Design Inc.

Creative Welding

Daniel Balyeat Landscaping

Dansky Handcrafted LLC

E2 Solar

Elite Plastering

Energy Conservation Insulation

Green Apple Construction

Guy Pettit Drywall

High Desert Hardwood Flooring

Kevin Spencer Masonry

Mckernan Enterprises Inc.

Moore Climate Control

Oregon Timberworks

Parazoo Plumbing

River Roofing

TVM Waterproofing

Versatile Carpentry

Your Garden Companion

# PHOTO CREDITS

**Chandler Photography, Bend, Oregon**

Pages 1, 8-9, 10-11, 20-21, 22-23, 34, 44-45, 67, 68-69, 70-71, 72-73,
88-89, 90-91, 95, 98, 104-105, 106-107, 109, 110, 114-115, 116, 126,
132-133, 134-135, 136-137, 144-145, 146-147, 150, 152, 156, 158-159, 169


**Dorothy Freudenberg, Bend, Oregon**

Pages 15, 48, 50-51, 52, 54-55, 56-57, 58, 60, 61,
62, 65, 74, 78, 82, 84-85, 86, 92, 100, 102-103, 111,
112, 122, 125, 127, 129, 130, 139, 149, 161


**Special Acknowledgement**

*Bend Bulletin*, Dean Guernsey, Photo Editor

## INTERNATIONAL
## LIVING FUTURE INSTITUTE

The International Living Future Institute is an environmental NGO committed to catalyzing the transformation toward communities that are socially just, culturally rich and ecologically restorative. The Institute is premised on the belief that providing a compelling vision for the future is a fundamental requirement for reconciling humanity's relationship with the natural world. The Institute operates the Living Building Challenge, the built environment's most rigorous performance standard, and Declare, an ingredients label for building materials. It houses the Cascadia Green Building Council and Ecotone Publishing.

## ECOTONE PUBLISHING

Founded by green building experts in 2004, Ecotone Publishing is dedicated to meeting the growing demand for authoritative and accessible books on sustainable design, materials selection and building techniques in North America and beyond. Located in the Cascadia region, Ecotone is well positioned to play an important part in the green design movement. Ecotone searches out and documents inspiring projects, visionary people and vital trends that are leading the design industry to transformational change toward a healthier planet.

## LIVING BUILDING CHALLENGE

The Living Building Challenge is the built environment's most rigorous performance standard. It calls for the creation of building projects at all scales that operate as cleanly, beautifully and efficiently as nature's architecture. To be certified under the Challenge, projects must meet a series of ambitious performance requirements, including net zero energy, waste and water, over a minimum of 12 months of continuous occupancy.